FATHER SERGIUS

AND OTHER STORIES AND
PLAYS

By COUNT LEO TOLSTOY

Edited by Dr. HAGBERG WRIGHT.

With an Introductory Essay by
AYLMER MAUDE.

THOMAS NELSON AND SONS
LONDON, EDINBURGH, DUBLIN
LEEDS, AND NEW YORK
LEIPZIG: 35-37 Königstrasse.   PARIS: 189, rue Saint-Jacques

First Published in 1911.

CONTENTS.

PREFACE.

TOLSTOY AS DRAMATIST.

IN almost every kind of literary work he touched, Tolstoy succeeded at once in reaching the foremost rank.

When he sent his first story, "Childhood," anonymously to the poet Nekrásov, editor of *The Contemporary* (then the leading Petersburg magazine), the latter promptly accepted and published it; Dostoyévsky was so struck by it that he wrote from Siberia to inquire who its talented author was; Turgénev sang its praises; and Panáev was so delighted with it that his friends, it was said, had to avoid him on the Névsky lest he should insist on reading them extracts from it.

When Tolstoy turned from stories to novels he achieved the same immediate and complete success. The appearance of the first instalment of "War and Peace" sufficed to place him abreast of the world's greatest writers of fiction.

Fourteen years later he turned to spiritual autobiography, and his " Confession " immediately took rank beside those of St. Augustine and Rousseau.

When he propounded his interpretation of Christ's teaching, his works produced a profound impression, and, though they were prohibited in Russia, found a large circulation abroad besides a surreptitious one at home.

Next he took to writing short, simple stories for the people, and the very first of these, " What Men live by " (v. " Twenty-three Tales "), circulated by hundreds of thousands of copies in Russia, was translated into all civilized languages, and delighted people, old and young, in the five continents.

When he turned his attention to social problems, and wrote " What then must we do ? " the book aroused the deepest interest wherever it was read, and was promptly recognized as one of the most remarkable studies of poverty ever penned.

He took to essays, and at once produced a series which many readers have declared to be as interesting and stimulating as any that were ever written.

Interested in the philosophy of art, he wrote "What is Art?" His preparation for this attempt to put art on a new basis took him, it is true, fifteen years, and a majority of critics everywhere denounced the opinions he expressed ; but, at any rate, there was no doubt about the general interest he aroused, and the longer the matter is discussed, the stronger grows the suspicion that on the main point of the discussion Tolstoy saw deeper than his critics, and that, great artist as he was, his philosophy of art as well as his practice of it was fundamentally sound.

Finally his philippics, such as his "Reply to the Synod," which had excommunicated him (v. "Essays and Letters"), and his denunciation of the Courts-martial in "I cannot be silent!" rang rang out with a sincerity, courage, and effectiveness unparalleled since Pascal's "Provincial Letters," or the famous theses Luther nailed to the church door at Wittenberg.

Only as a dramatist did Tolstoy fail at his first attempt; and even in that direction success came so promptly that it is his success rather than his failure that surprises one.

As a seventeen-year-old student at Kazán University, he had taken part with much success in two plays given for some charity at Carnival time; and his taste for theatricals did not soon pass, for in later years, when writing of the time after his return from the defence of Sevastopol, and telling of the death of his brother Demetrius, he adds: "I really believe that what hurt me most was that his death prevented my taking part in some private theatricals then being got up at Court, and to which I had been invited."

While living in Petersburg and Moscow as a young man, Tolstoy was enthusiastic in his admiration of one of the great Russian actors of those days. But he never lived much in cities, and probably no other great dramatist ever spent so little time in the theatre as he did. In that, as in many other lines of work, his quickness of perception, tenacity of memory, and vividness of emotion enabled him to dispense with the long training men of less genius require.

In 1863, soon after his marriage, he wrote two plays which were never published. One, a farcical comedy called *The Nihilist*, was privately performed with much success. The other, also a comedy, called *The Infected Family*, he intended for public performance. With that end in view Tolstoy took it to Moscow early in 1864. The theatrical season (which in Russia ends at the beginning of Lent) was then, however, too far advanced for any manager to stage the piece that winter ; and as it dealt with a topic of the day which lost some of its freshness by keeping, Tolstoy never afterwards offered it to any one.

That was the one and only rebuff he ever had to face in his literary career, if one excepts the amusing incident of his sending a short prose poem anonymously to a Moscow newspaper, and receiving it back declined with thanks, on the ground that its author was "not yet sufficiently expert in expression !" For the next six years he seems not to have taken any interest in the drama ; but in 1870 we find him writing to Fet :—

"There is much, very much, I want to tell you about. I have been reading a lot of Shakespear, Goethe, Púshkin, Gógol and Molière, and about all of them there is much I want to say to you."

A few days later he again wrote to the same friend :—

"You want to read me a story of cavalry life. . . . And I don't want to read you anything, because I am not writing anything ; but I very much want to talk about Shakespear and Goethe, and the drama in general. This whole winter I am occupied only with the drama ; and it happens to me as usually happens to people who, till they are forty, have not thought of a certain subject, or formed any conception of it, and then suddenly, with forty-year-old clearness, turn their attention to this new, untasted subject—it seems to them that they discern in it much that is new. All winter I have enjoyed myself lying down, drowsing, playing bézique, snow-shoeing, skating, and, most of all, lying in bed [ill] while characters from a drama or comedy have performed for me. And they perform very well. It is about that I want to talk to you. In that, as in everything, you are a classic and understand the essence of the matter very deeply. I should like also to read Sophocles and Euripides."

The mood passed, and for another fifteen years one hears no more about it : Tolstoy being absorbed first in the production of an "ABC Book" for school-children, then with "Anna Karénina," then with his "Confession" and religious studies, as well as with field-work, hutbuilding, and bootmaking.

Early in 1886, noting the wretched character of the plays given in the booths at the Carnival shows on the Maidens' Field just outside Moscow, not far from his own house, and feeling how wrong it was that the dramatic food of the people should consist of the crudest melodramas, he was moved to turn into a play a small Temperance story he had written. This piece, called *The First Distiller*, is of no great importance in itself, but was the precursor of the splendid dramas he soon afterwards produced.

The following summer, while out ploughing, he hurts his leg, neglects it, and gets erysipelas, which almost leads to blood-poisoning. His life is in imminent danger, he has to undergo a painful operation, is laid up for weeks, and while ill writes most of *The Power of Darkness*, an immensely powerful play which serves as a touchstone for those who have the Tolstoy feeling in them.

From the poisoning of Peter, the husband, in the beginning, to the murder of the baby in the middle, and Nikíta's arrest at the end, the piece is full of horrors which most people, who do not look at things from Tolstoy's point of view, find it wellnigh impossible to endure. To them the play appears to be one of unmitigated blackness. To Tolstoyans it is not so. The lies, the crimes, the horrors are there, as in real life ; but in the play one sees more clearly than in common life the clue to the meaning of it all. When Nikíta's conscience begins to be touched ; when Mítritch, the old soldier, teaches him not to be afraid of men ; and finally, when Akím, the old father, rejoices that his son has confessed, the heavens open and the purpose of life—the preparing for what is yet to come by getting things straight here and now—is revealed, and the effect of the play, instead of being sordid or painful, becomes inspiring.

The play was founded on fact, though what happened in real life was even more gruesome, for in actual fact Nikíta's prototype, when on the point of driving off to Akulína's wedding, suddenly seized a large wooden wedge and aimed a tremendous blow at her younger sister ; and he did this not out of malice, but because he felt so sure that it is a misfortune to be alive in a world where things have gone so wrong as they have done in the world we live in. Fortunately his blow, which seemed certain to kill the girl, glanced aside, and merely stunned her without doing her any permanent injury.

The Power of Darkness was prohibited by the Dramatic Censor, and throughout the reign of Alexander III. its public performance in Russia was forbidden.

It was produced for the first time at the Théâtre Libre in Paris in February 1888. Among its most enthusiastic admirers was Zola, who was as anxious about it as he could have been had it been his own work. "Above all, do not strike out a single scene or a single word, and do not fear for its success," said he at one of the rehearsals; and he was quite right. The piece had a tremendous success, and was played at one and the same time at three different Paris theatres, as well as at the Freie Bühnen in Berlin, where it had a similar triumph. After the accession of Nicholas II. it was acted in Russia, and took rank at once as one of the greatest masterpieces of Russian dramatic art, and as such holds a place in the repertory of the best Moscow and Petersburg theatres.

Many Englishmen who have seen it have been immensely impressed by it. Laurence Irving wrote me : "I suppose England is the only country in Europe where *The Power of Darkness* has not been acted. It ought to be done. It is a stupendous tragedy ; the effect on the stage is unparalleled." Bernard Shaw, writing to Tolstoy, said : "I remember nothing in the whole range of drama that fascinated me more than the old soldier in your *Power of Darkness*. One of the things that struck me in that play was the feeling that the preaching of the old man, right as he was, could never be of any use—that it could only anger his son and rub the last grains of self-respect out of him. But what the pious and good father could not do, the old rascal of a soldier did as if he was the voice of God. To me that scene where the two drunkards are wallowing in the straw and the older rascal lifts the younger one above his cowardice and his selfishness, has an intensity of effect that no merely romantic scene could possibly attain." Arthur Symons wrote : "More than any play I have ever seen, this astounding play of Tolstoy's seems to me to fulfil Aristotle's demand upon tragedy : 'Through pity and fear effecting the proper purgation of these emotions.' I had never read it ; my impression was gained directly from seeing it on the

stage. Well (though as I listened to it I felt the
pity and fear to be almost insupportable) I left
the theatre with a feeling of exultation, as I have
left a concert room after hearing a piece of noble
and tragic music. How out of such human dis-
cords such a divine harmony can be woven I do
not know—that is the secret of Tolstoy's genius,
as it is the secret of the musician's. Here,
achieved in terms of naked horror, I found some
of the things that Maeterlinck has aimed at and
never quite rendered through an atmosphere and
through forms of vague beauty. And I found
also another kind of achievement, by the side
of which Ibsen's cunning adjustments of reality
seemed either trivial or unreal. Here, for once,
human life is islanded on the stage, a pin-point
of light in an immense darkness ; and the sense
of that surrounding darkness is conveyed to us
as in no other play that I have ever seen, by an
awful sincerity and by an unparalleled simplicity.
Whether Tolstoy has learnt by instinct some
stage-craft which playwrights have been toiling
after in vain, or by what conscious and deliberate
art he has supplemented instinct, I do not know.
But out of horror and humour, out of the dregs
of human life and out of mere faith in those dregs,
somehow, as a man of genius does once in an
age, Tolstoy has in this play made for us the

great modern play, the great play of the nineteenth century."

That Tolstoy should thus have begun successful play-writing at a time when he was supposed
to have turned aside from art, and when he was
nearly sixty years of age, was remarkable ; but at
any rate *The Power of Darkness* was a serious piece,
obviously dealing with moral questions which stirred
his soul profoundly at the time : and, moreover,
he wrote it for the People's Theatre, started to
provide first-rate drama for the peasants. It came,
therefore, as a yet greater surprise to many people
when, three years later, he was persuaded by his
daughters to write a comedy for them to perform
at home, at Yásnaya Polyána.

One knows pretty well how it happened. The
taste for play-writing was strong upon him. After
more than twelve years devoted to didactic work
which gave his sense of humour little or no scope,
it was in the nature of things that he should feel
some reaction.

At first the play was to have been only a
short two-act affair. He did not like to refuse
his daughters' request, and thought that if they
must act something, it was better that they should
act a play voicing his contempt for the follies and
extravagance of society and his consciousness of
the peasants' needs. Once started on the work,

however, it took hold of him, and grew and grew till it became a full-fledged four-act comedy with over thirty speaking characters in it, and with the didactic purpose overwhelmed by the fun, the bustle, and the stage-craft of it.

After many rehearsals this play, *Fruits of Culture*, was performed at Yásnaya Polyána on December 30, 1889, with immense success. Tánya, Tolstoy's eldest daughter, took the part of her namesake in the play very successfully, and Mary, his second daughter, played the cook most admirably.

Tolstoy himself heartily enjoyed the performance. One greatly respects his thirty-year struggle to live a simple life, consuming little and giving much; but one does not love him the less for the occasional lapses into whole-hearted gaiety which light up the record of his life, and show us how very human was this giant. Yásnaya Polyána on New Year's Eve 1889, crammed with guests all in the highest spirits, the large upstairs room full of spectators laughing till their sides ached at Tolstoy's comedy, is a scene those who would understand Tolstoy should by no means forget or despise. Yet even then the other side of his nature, which never let him rest, caused him to note in his Diary : "I am ashamed of all this expense in the midst of poverty."

The whole company threw themselves into the

piece with enthusiasm, and acted really well. In particular, V. M. Lopátin, a neighbouring Justice of the Peace, extracted from the part of the Third Peasant so much more than its author had anticipated, or even intended, that Tolstoy, in ecstasies, slapped his thighs and laughed till the tears rolled down his cheeks; for he was always extremely susceptible to anything really good, whether in acting or in other forms of art.

I well remember meeting at Yásnaya Polyána, on two different occasions, the sculptor Ginzburg, who was an admirable mimic. He could keep a room full of people entranced while he enacted a Jew tailor stitching clothes, or a nurse tending or neglecting an imaginary baby. None of those present expressed warmer admiration of these performances than did Tolstoy himself, and when he went for a walk with us afterwards, he said to Ginzburg with great animation :

"Ah, if our theatre realists could only be got to understand that what is wanted is not to put real babies on the stage or show the real messes they make, but to convey, as you do, by voice and feature, the real feeling that has to be expressed!"

No blunder made by Tolstoy's critics is more gratuitous or indefensible than the pretence that he was indifferent to the form of art, or demanded of it that it should always have a directly didactic intention.

Not without express purpose did he, in "What is Art?" write: "Art is a means of union among men, joining them together in the same feelings, and indispensable for the life and progress towards well-being of individuals and of humanity;" and he then goes on to say: "Thanks to man's capacity to be infected with the feelings of others by means of art, all that is being lived through by his contemporaries is accessible to him, as well as the feelings experienced by men thousands of years ago, and he has also the possibility of transmitting his own feelings to others.

"If men lacked this capacity of being infected by art, people would be more separated and hostile to one another, and more savage than wild beasts. Therefore the activity of art is a most important one—as important as the activity of speech itself, and as generally diffused." And in a memorable passage he adds: "We are accustomed to understand art to be only what we hear and see in theatres, concerts, and exhibitions; together with buildings, statues, poems, novels. . . . But all this is but the smallest part of the art by which we communicate with each other in life. All human life is filled with works of art of every kind—from cradle-song, jest, mimicry, the ornamentation of houses, dress, and utensils, up to church services, buildings, monuments, and triumphal processions. It is all artistic activity."

He insists again and again on the value and prevalence of art, and when speaking of those primitive Christians and others who have wished to repudiate art, he says, " Evidently such people were wrong in repudiating all art, for they denied that which cannot be denied—one of the indispensable means of communication without which mankind could not exist."

Tolstoy knew very well that a performance must be excellent in its form and method of expression in order to be a work of art. In the illustration he gives of the performance of music, for instance, he says that for musical execution to be artistic and to transmit feeling, many conditions are necessary, of which the three chief are the pitch, the time, and the strength of the sound, and he adds : " Musical execution is only then art, only then infects, when the sound is neither higher nor lower than it should be—that is, when exactly the infinitely small centre of the required note is taken, when that note is continued exactly as long as needed, and when the strength of the sound is neither more nor less than is required. The slightest deviation of pitch in either direction, the slightest increase or decrease in time, or the slightest strengthening or weakening of the sound beyond what is needed, destroys the perfection, and, consequently, the infectiousness of the work. So that the feeling of infection by the art of music, which seems so simple and so easily obtained, is a thing we receive only when the performer finds those infinitely minute degrees which are necessary to perfection in music. It is the same in all arts: a wee bit lighter, a wee bit darker, a wee bit higher, lower, to the right or the left, in painting— a wee bit weaker or stronger in intonation, or a wee bit sooner or later, in dramatic art—a wee bit omitted, over-emphasized, or exaggerated, in poetry—and there is no contagion. It is only obtained when an artist finds those infinitely minute degrees of which a work of art consists, and only to the extent to which he finds them."

Confronted by words such as these, it is amazing that any one can pretend that Tolstoy was indifferent to quality in the forms of art; but not less amazing is the assertion that only what is directly moralizing was considered by him fit subject-matter for art. On this point his words are decisive when he includes among the subject-matter suitable for good art "the simplest feelings of common life."

The truth is that, in spite of certain prepossessions which tend to confuse the matter, and in spite of his pugnacious controversial methods, which often led to recrimination rather than to elucidation, Tolstoy's greatness as an artist was increased by the fact that he thoroughly understood the aim and purpose of art ; and he was able to speak with authority on the philosophy of art just because he was one of the most intellectual and intelligent of the world's artists.

As mentioned in my "Life of Tolstoy," the main theme in *Fruits of Culture* was drawn from Tolstoy's acquaintance with the Lvóvs, a wealthy and aristocratic family, the head of which wished to convert Tolstoy to spiritualism. The latter sturdily maintained a sceptical attitude, arguing that since mankind has been at the pains to discriminate between *matter* (which can be investigated by the five senses) and *spirit* (which is an affair of the conscience, and cannot be investigated by the senses), we must not again confuse the two by attempting to find physical evidence of spiritual existence. If the phenomena we are investigating is cognizable by the senses, then, he argued, such phenomena are, *ipso facto*, not spiritual, but material. In this, as in certain other matters, Tolstoy, seeking clearness, painted in black and white, and shunned those delicate shades which often elude and perplex us—but without which, after all, it is not always possible to get a true picture.

Fruits of Culture found its way on to the public stage in Russia before *The Power of Darkness*, and both there and abroad the two plays have been almost equally successful. It is often treated as pure comedy, and the peasants presented as simply comic characters. This Tolstoy did not intend, and did not like. He meant the hardness of their lot and their urgent need of land to stand out in sharp contrast to the waste of wealth by the cultured crowd.

During the last thirty years of his life Tolstoy himself used, as is well known, to dress much like a peasant, though never in the beggar-pilgrim garb in which he is made to figure in a "Life" of him recently published in this country ; and it happened that one winter's day, when *Fruits of Culture* was being rehearsed in Túla (the nearest town to Yásnaya Polyána), he went, by request, to the hall where it was being staged. Wearing his rough sheepskin overcoat, he attempted to enter, but was roughly shoved out by the doorkeeper, who told him it was no place for the likes of him !

The same year the play was presented at Tsarskoye Selo by amateurs drawn from the highest circles of Court society, and was witnessed by a dozen Grand-Dukes and Grand-Duchesses as well as by the Tsar himself, who warmly thanked the performers for the pleasure it had given him.

So the whirligig of time brought it about that Tolstoy, who twenty-three years before had just missed his chance of acting at the Imperial Court, now had a play of his own performed there, while he himself was being mistaken for a peasant, and on that account treated with gross indignity.

We have Tolstoy's word for it that he would have written more plays had it not been for the Censor. He once said: "I feel certain the Censor would not pass my plays. You would not believe how, from the very commencement of my activity, that horrible Censor question has tormented me! I wanted to write what I felt; but at the same time it occurred to me that what I wrote would not be permitted, and involuntarily I had to abandon the work. I abandoned, and went on abandoning, and meanwhile the years passed away."

He once expressed surprise that in *Fruits of Culture* the drunken man-cook's monologue on the ways of the rich folk was allowed to be performed.

Of the three plays left by Tolstoy for publication after his death, one is a short two-act Temperance play called in English *The Cause of it All* (the Russian title is a colloquialism difficult to render, but "From it all evil flows" is as near as one can get to it). It does not claim to be a of much importance, but if ever it is staged it should act easily and well.

Another of these posthumous plays is *The Man who was dead* (The Live Corpse), a powerful piece, in which Tolstoy introduces one of those gipsy choirs which had such an influence on him (and still more on his brother Sergius) when he was a young man of twenty to twenty-three, before he went to the Caucasus and entered the army.

The position of the gipsy choirs in Russia is a peculiar one. Reputedly Egyptian in origin ("Pharaoh's Tribe," one of the characters in the play calls them), they live a life quite distinct from that of the Russians, yet not at all resembling that of the itinerant gipsies one meets travelling about with caravans in England. They possess a remarkable musical talent, having a kind of music, both vocal and instrumental, all their own. They perform at special restaurants in the suburbs of Moscow, and also give concerts in public halls and at private houses. It is no more unusual for Russian noblemen to marry gipsy girls than it is for English noblemen to marry Gaiety girls. The songs referred to in Scene II. are all well-known gipsy songs ; and if staged with a real gipsy choir to perform them, this should be one of the most striking scenes in the play.

Tolstoy himself held that gipsy music deserved

to rank among the best kinds of music, on account of its genuine spontaneity, the depth of feeling in it, and the exquisite perfection with which it is rendered by the gipsies. His own daughters used to play and sing gipsy songs admirably.

The main plot of this play, like that of *The Power of Darkness*, was supplied to Tolstoy by his friend N. V. Davýdov, a Judge and a Lecturer on Criminal Law at Moscow University, who frequently drew his attention to cases that occurred in the Law Courts, and which Davýdov thought might provide suitable subjects for a story or a drama.

Curiously enough, after Tolstoy had written this play, he was visited first by the stepson of the "live corpse," and then by the "live corpse" himself. The latter had been convicted, had served his time, and had returned to Moscow. He had given up drink and was seeking means of subsistence, when he heard of the play Tolstoy was writing, and that it was founded on his own case. Tolstoy questioned him carefully, and as a result of the conversation rewrote the play in order to set the conduct of the corpse in a more favourable light than before. In this revised version Tolstoy makes him finally commit suicide, whereas in an earlier version the law took its course as it did in real life, and matters only settled down and adjusted themselves after its victims had served their sentences and justice had ceased to meddle.

Tolstoy also gave the "corpse" a letter to Davýdov, who obtained for him some small post at the Law Courts, where he served till his death, no one but his benefactors and his own family knowing who he was. Some time after his death Davýdov told me this about him.

Part of the attraction of the story for Tolstoy lay in the fact that the intervention of the law did no good to any one, but only harm to all concerned ; for it was part and parcel of Tolstoy's non-resistant theory that Law Courts and the Administration of Justice are purely noxious.

The Man who was dead has already been staged at the Artistic Theatre in Moscow, and it is to be hoped that we shall see it in London ; but the last of Tolstoy's plays, *The Light that shines in Darkness*, was left unfinished, and is hardly likely to be produced, unless by the Stage Society or some similar organization. In Russia it is prohibited on account of its allusions to the refusal of military service.

Yet it is in some ways the most interesting of Tolstoy's posthumous works. It is obviously not strictly autobiographical, for Tolstoy was not assassinated, as the hero of the piece is, nor was his daughter engaged to be married to a young prince who refused military service. But, like some of his other writings, the play is semi-autobiographical. In it not only has Tolstoy utilized personal experiences, but, more than that, he answers the question so often asked: Why, holding his views, did he not free himself from property before he grew old?

Some people, and especially some of those most devoted to Tolstoy's memory, are sure to suppose, and to declare, that he intends Nicholas Ivanovich Sarintsev to be taken as a faithful portrait of himself. But to understand Tolstoy one has to recognize the duality of his character, which he never concealed and often mentioned; and the hero of *The Light that shines in Darkness* has none of this duality. He represents only one side of Tolstoy, and is not at all the sort of man, for instance, who would have written or enjoyed *Fruits of Culture*.

Not only are the facts different to the real ones, and the character of the hero much simpler than Tolstoy's own, but the problem at issue between Sarintsev and his wife is not quite the same as the one at issue between Tolstoy and the Countess. With that unerring artistic tact which Tolstoy never lost, he causes Nicholas Ivanovich Sarintsev to make a definite proposal to retain "fifty acres and the kitchen garden and the flooded meadow," which would "bring in about £50 a year." Now

what in real life most frightened the Countess was
not that she was asked to accept poverty, but that
she was asked to manage a household in which
there should be no limit to the giving up.

Tolstoy held, as he says in *The Demands of Love*,
that if people begin giving up and set any limits
thereto, then "life will be hell, or will become
hell, if they are not hypocrites. . . . Where and
how can one stop? Only those will find a stopping-place who are strangers to the feeling of the
reality of the brotherhood of man, or who are so
accustomed to lie that they no longer notice the
difference between truth and falsehood. The fact
is, no such stopping-place can exist. . . . If you
give the beggar your last shillings, you will be left
without bread to-morrow ; but to refuse, means to
turn from that for the sake of which one lives."

Had that point, and the need of admitting to
one's cottage "the tramp with his lice and his
typhus," and giving away the children's last cup
of milk, been pressed home in the play as it was in
Tolstoy's teaching, some of the readers' sympathy
would go over to the side of the wife called on to
face such conditions for herself and her family ;
and that is why Tolstoy's artistic instinct induced
him to introduce a definite proposal quite at
variance with the demands of his own teaching.

And again, the conflict in the play is between

the husband on the one side and the wife and family on the other. There is no mention of a friend urging the husband on in opposition to the wife ; but those who closely followed Tolstoy's own fate well know that on this point also the play does not describe his own case.

Not the less on that account does the play most touchingly present to us the intense tragedy of Tolstoy's later years, and the impossibility in which he found himself of acting so as neither to violate his own conscience nor to evoke anger in the hearts of those nearest to him. His religion had brought "not peace, but a sword ; " and it was because he believed in it so firmly, and yet shrank from treating those of his own household as his foes, that his struggle was so intense, and that for more than thirty years he hesitated before he decided to leave wife and home, the scenes endeared to him by childhood's memory, and the spot where he hoped to be (and eventually was) buried—the spot where his brother had hidden the green stick on which he said was inscribed the secret of how to banish from the world all sin, bitterness, discord, and evil—all, in short, that makes us sad or sorry.

Plays Tolstoy found more difficult to write than stories or novels ; for in the novel or story it is

possible to stop and explain, and gradually to prepare
an incident or develop a character, whereas in a
play the situations and clash of characters and
wills have to be presented ripe and ready.   Novel-
writing he compared to painting, in which many
shades may be employed ; plays he compared to
sculpture, where all must be clear-cut, definite, and
compact.

He often remarked that subjects suitable for
novels are not suitable for plays, and *vice versâ ;*
and he expressed satisfaction that he had never
been obliged to witness the dramatized versions of
"Resurrection" or of "Anna Karénina" which have
been staged.   He had nothing at all to do with
those productions, and quite disapproved of them.

Of his plays in general Tolstoy once remarked
to me, " When writing them I never anticipated
the importance that has been attributed to them."
While he fully recognized, and perhaps at times
overrated, the value of his didactic and propa-
gandist writings, he was often inclined to under-
rate the value of the artistic work, which during
his later years he sometimes undertook more or
less as a recreation, and on that account was the
more ready to treat lightly.

AYLMER MAUDE.

FATHER SERGIUS.

FATHER SERGIUS.

I.

THERE happened in Petersburg during the 'forties an event which startled society.

A handsome youth, a prince, an officer in the Cuirassiers, for whom every one had predicted the rank of aide-de-camp and a brilliant career attached to the person of Emperor Nicholas I., quitted the service. He broke with his beautiful *fiancée*, a lady-in-waiting, and a favourite of the Empress, just a fortnight before the wedding-day, and giving his small estate to his sister, retired to a monastery to become a monk.

To those who were ignorant of the hidden motives this was an extraordinary and unaccountable step; but as regards Prince Stephen Kasatsky himself, it was such a natural move that he could not conceive an alternative.

His father, a retired colonel of the Guards, died when the son was twelve. Although it was hard for his mother to let him go from her, she would

2

not act in defiance of the wishes of her late husband, who had expressed the desire that in the event of his death the boy should be sent away and educated as a cadet. So she secured his admission to the corps.

The widow herself, with her daughter Varvara, moved to Petersburg in order to be in the same town with the boy and to take him home for his holidays. He showed brilliant capacity and extraordinary ambition, and came out first in military drill, in riding, and in his studies —mathematics especially, for which he had a particular liking.

In spite of his abnormal height he was a handsome, graceful lad, and had it not been for his violent temper he would have been an altogether exemplary cadet. He never drank or indulged in any sort of dissipation, and he was particularly truthful. The fits of fury which maddened him from time to time, when he lost all control over himself and raged like a wild animal, were the only faults in his character. Once, when a cadet ragged him because of his collection of minerals, he almost threw the boy out of the window. On another occasion he rushed at an officer and struck him, it was said, for having broken his word and told a direct lie.

For this he would surely have been degraded

to the rank of a common soldier, if it had not been for the head of the school, who hushed up the matter and dismissed the officer.

At eighteen Kasatsky left with the rank of lieutenant, and entered an aristocratic Guard regiment. The Emperor Nicholas had known him while he was in the cadet corps, and had shown him favour while in the regiment. It was on this account that people prophesied that he would become an aide-de-camp. Kasatsky desired it greatly, although less from ambition than from passionate love for the Emperor which he had cherished since his cadet days. Each time the Emperor visited the school—and he visited it very often—as Kasatsky saw the tall figure, the broad chest, the aquiline nose above the moustache, and the close-cropped side whiskers, the military uniform, and the brisk, firm step, and heard him greeting the cadets in his strident voice, he experienced the momentary ecstasy of one who sees his well-beloved. But his passionate adoration of the Emperor was even more intense. He desired to give up something, everything, even himself, to show his infinite devotion. The Emperor Nicholas knew that he inspired such admiration, and deliberately provoked it. He played with the cadets, made them surround him, and treated them sometimes with childish simplicity, sometimes as a friend, and then again with an air of solemn grandeur.

After the incident with the officer, the Emperor, who did not allude to it, waved Kasatsky theatrically aside when the latter approached him. Then, when he was leaving, he frowned and shook his finger at the boy, saying, "Be assured that everything is known to me; but there are things I do not wish to know. Nevertheless they are *here*," and he pointed to his heart.

When the cadets were formally received by the Emperor on leaving the school, he did not remind Kasatsky of his insubordination, but told them all, as was his custom, that they could turn to him in need, that they were to serve him and their country with loyalty, and that he would ever remain their best friend. All were touched, as usual; and Kasatsky, remembering the past, shed tears, and made a vow to serve his beloved Tsar with all his might.

When Kasatsky entered the regiment his mother and sister left Petersburg, going first to Moscow and then to their estate in the country. Kasatsky gave half his fortune to his sister. What remained was quite sufficient to support him in the expensive regiment which he had joined.

Viewed from outside, Kasatsky seemed like an ordinary brilliant young officer of the Guards making a career for himself. But within his soul there were intense and complex strivings. Although this striving, which had been going on ever since his childhood, seemed to vary in its nature, it was essentially one and the same, and had for its object that absolute perfection in every undertaking which would give him the applause and admiration of the world. Whatever it might be, accomplishments or learning, he worked to merit praise and to stand as an example to the rest. Mastering one subject he took up another, and so obtained first place in his studies. For example, while he was still in the corps, conscious of a lack of fluency in his French, he contrived to master the language so that he knew it like his own. Then again, when he became interested in chess while still in the corps, he worked at the game till he acquired proficiency.

Apart from the chief end of life, which was in his eyes the service of the Tsar and his country, he had always some self-appointed aim ; and however unimportant it might be, he pursued this with his whole soul, and lived for it until it was accomplished. But the moment it was attained another arose in its place. This passion for distinguishing himself and for pursuing an object in order to distinguish himself filled his life. So it was that after entering upon his career he set himself to acquire the utmost perfection in the knowledge of the service, and, except for his uncontrollable temper, which was sometimes the occasion of actions that were inimical to his success, he soon became a model officer.

Once during a conversation in society he realized the need of a more general education : so, setting himself to work to read books, he soon attained what he desired. Then he wanted to hold a brilliant position in aristocratic society : he learned to dance beautifully, and was presently invited to all the balls and parties in the best circles. But he was not satisfied with this : he was accustomed to being first in everything, and in this instance he was very far from that. Society at that time consisted, as I suppose it has done in every time and place, of four kinds of people—rich people who are received at Court ; people who are not rich, but are born and brought up in Court circles ; rich people who ape the Court ; and people, neither rich nor of the Court, who copy both.

Kasatsky did not belong to the first two, but was gladly received in the last two sets. On entering society his first idea was that he must have a *liaison* with a society lady ; and quite unexpectedly it soon came about. Presently, however, he realized that the circle in which he moved was not the most exclusive, and that there were higher spheres, and that, notwithstanding he was received there, he was a stranger in their midst. They were polite to him, but their manner made it plain that they had their own intimates, and that he was not one of them. Kasatsky longed to be one of them. To attain this end he must become an aide-de-camp—which he expected to be—or else he must marry into the set. He resolved upon this latter course. His choice fell upon a young girl, a beauty, belonging to the Court, and not merely belonging to the circle he wished to move in, whose society was coveted by the most distinguished and the most firmly rooted in this circle. This was the Countess Korotkova. Kasatsky began to pay court to her purely for the sake of his career ; she was uncommonly attractive, and he very soon fell in love with her. She was noticeably cool towards him at first, and then suddenly everything changed. She treated him graciously, and her mother continually invited him to the house.

Kasatsky proposed, and was accepted. He was rather astonished at the facility with which he gained his happiness, and he noticed something strange in the behaviour towards him of both mother and daughter. He was deeply in love, and love had made him blind, so he failed to realize what nearly the whole town knew—that the previous year his *fiancée* had been the favourite of the Emperor Nicholas.

Two weeks before the day arranged for the wedding Kasatsky was at Tsarskoye Selo, at the country place of his *fiancée*. It was a hot day in May. The lovers had had a walk in the garden, and were sitting on a bench in the shade of the lindens. Mary looked exceedingly pretty in her white muslin dress. She seemed the personification of love and innocence—now bending her head, now gazing at her handsome young lover, who was talking to her with great tenderness and self-restraint, as though he feared by look or gesture to offend her angelic purity. Kasatsky belonged to those men of the 'forties who do not exist nowadays, who deliberately, while condoning impurity in themselves, require in their wives the most ideal and seraphic innocence. Being prepared to find this purity in every girl of their set, they behaved accordingly. This theory, in so far as it concerned the laxity which the men permitted themselves, was certainly altogether wrong and harmful ; but in its relation to the women, I think, compared with the notion of the modern young man who sees in every girl nothing but a mate or a female, there was much to be said for it. The girls, perceiving such adoration, endeavoured with more or less success to be goddesses.

Kasatsky held the views of his time, and looked with such eyes upon his sweetheart. That day he was more in love than ever, but there was nothing sensual in his feelings towards his *fiancée*. On the contrary, he regarded her with the tender adoration of something unattainable. He rose and stood at his full height before her, leaning with both hands on his sabre.

"Now for the first time I know what happiness is. And it is you—darling—who have given me that happiness," he said, smiling shyly.

He was still at that stage where endearments are not yet a habit, and it made him gasp to think of using them to such an angel.

"It is you who have made me see myself clearly. You have shown me that I am better than I thought," he added.

"I knew it long ago. That is what made me begin to love you."

The nightingales were beginning their song somewhere near and the young leaves moved in the sudden gusts of wind. He raised her hand to his lips and there were tears in his eyes.

She understood that he was thanking her for having said that she loved him. He took a few steps backwards and forwards, remaining silent, then approached her again, and sat beside her.

"You know, when I began to make love to

you, it was not disinterested on my part. I wanted
to get into society. And then, when I came to
know you better, how little all that mattered, compared to you! Are you angry with me for that?"

She did not answer, but touched his hand. He
understood that it meant " I am not angry."

"Well, you said——" he stopped. It seemed too
bold to say what he intended. " You said—that
you—began to love me—forgive me—I quite
believe it—but there is something that troubles
you and stands in the way of your feelings. What
is it?"

"Yes—now or never," she thought. "He
will know it anyhow. But now he will not forsake me because of it. Oh, if he should, how
dreadful!" And she gazed with deep affection
upon that tall, noble, powerful figure. She loved
him now more than the Tsar, and were it not for
Nicholas being an emperor, her choice between
them would rest on Kasatsky.

"Listen," she said. "I cannot deceive you; I
must tell you everything. You asked me what
stood in the way. It is that I have loved before."

She again laid her hand on his with an imploring gesture.

He was silent.

"Do you want to know who it was? The
Emperor."

"We all loved him. I can imagine you, a schoolgirl in the institute——"

"No. After that. It was only a passing infatuation, but I must tell you——"

"Well—what?"

"No, it was not simply——" She covered her face with her hands.

"What! You gave yourself to him?"

She was silent.

"His mistress?"

Still she did not answer.

He sprang to his feet, and pale as death, with his teeth chattering, stood before her. He now remembered how the Emperor, meeting him on the Nevsky, had congratulated him.

"O my God, what have I done? Stephen!"

"Don't touch me—don't touch me! Oh, how terrible!"

He turned and went to the house. There he met her mother.

"What's the matter with you, prince?"

She stopped, seeing his face.

The blood rushed suddenly to his head.

"You knew it! And you wanted me to shield them! Oh, if you weren't a woman——" he shouted, raising his large fist. Then he turned and ran away.

Had the lover of his *fiancée* been a private

individual he would have killed him.   But it was his beloved Tsar.

The next day he asked for furlough and then for his discharge.   Feigning illness, he refused to see any one, and went away to the country.

There he spent the summer putting his affairs in order.   When summer was over he did not return to Petersburg, but entered a monastery with the intention of becoming a monk.

His mother wrote to dissuade him from this momentous step.   He answered that he felt a vocation for God which was above all other considerations.   It was only his sister, who was as proud and ambitious as himself, who understood him.

She was quite right in her estimate of his motives.   His becoming a monk was only to show his contempt for all that seemed most important to the rest of the world, and had seemed so to himself while he was still an officer.   He climbed to a pinnacle from which he could look down on those he had previously envied.   However, contrary to his sister's opinion, this was not the only guiding motive.   Mingled with his pride and his passion for ascendancy there was also a genuine religious sentiment which Varvara did not know he possessed.   His sense of injury and his disappointment in Mary, whom he had thought

such an angel, were so poignant that they led him
to despair. His despair led where? To God,
to faith, to a childish faith which had never been
destroyed.

II.

On the feast of the Intercession of the Virgin,
Kasatsky entered the monastery, to show his
superiority over all those who fancied themselves above him.

The abbot was a nobleman by birth, a learned
man, and a writer. He belonged to that monastic
order which hails from Walachia, the members of
which choose, and in their turn are chosen, leaders
to be followed unswervingly and implicitly obeyed.

This abbot was the disciple of the famous
Ambrosius, disciple of Makardix of the Leonidas,
disciple of Païssy Velichkovsky.

To this abbot Kasatsky submitted himself as to
the superior of his choice.

Besides the feeling of ascendancy over others
which Kasatsky felt in the monastery as he had
felt it in the world, he found here the joy of
attaining perfection in the highest degree, inwardly
as well as outwardly. As in the regiment he had
rejoiced in being more than an irreproachable

officer, even exceeding his duties, so as a monk his endeavour was to be perfect, industrious, abstemious, meek, and humble: and above all, pure, not only in deed but in thought; and obedient. This last quality made his life there far easier. In that much-frequented monastery there were many conditions objectionable to him, but through obedience he became reconciled to them all.

"It is not for me to reason; I have but to obey, whatever the command." On guard before the sacred relics, singing in the choir, or adding up accounts in the hostelry, all possibility of doubt was silenced by obedience to his superior. Had it not been for that, the monotony and length of the church service, the intrusion of visitors, and the inferiority of the other monks would have been extremely distasteful to him. But, as it was, he bore it all perfectly, and found it even a solace and a support.

"I don't know," he thought, "why I ought to hear the same prayers many times a day, but I know that it is necessary; and knowing this, I rejoice." His superior had told him that as food is necessary for the life of the body, so is spiritual food, such as prayers in church, necessary for maintaining the life of the spirit. He believed it, and though he found the service for which he had to rise at a very early hour a difficulty, it brought him indubitable comfort and joy. This was the result of humility and the certainty that anything done in obedience to the superior was right.

The aim of his life was neither the gradual attainment of utter subjugation of his will, nor the attainment of greater and greater humility, but the achievement of all those Christian virtues which seemed in the beginning so easy of possession.

Being not in the least half-hearted, he gave what fortune remained to him to the monastery without regret.

Humility before his inferiors, far from being difficult, was a delight to him. Even the victory over the sins of greed and lust were easy for him. The superior had especially warned him against this latter sin, but Kasatsky was glad to feel immunity from it. He was only tortured by the thought of his *fiancée*. It was not only the thought of what had been, but the vivid picture of what might have been. He could not resist recalling to himself the image of the famous mistress of the Emperor, who afterwards married and became a good wife and mother. Her husband had a high position, influence, and esteem, and a good and penitent wife.

In his better hours Kasatsky was not distressed

by this thought. At such times he rejoiced that these temptations were past. But there were moments when all that went to make up his present life grew dark before his mind; moments when, if he did not actually cease to believe in the foundation of his present life, he was at least unable to perceive it; when he could not discover the object of his present life; when he was overcome with recollections of the past, and, terrible to say, with regret at having abandoned the world. His only salvation in that state of mind was obedience, and work, and prayers the whole day long. He went through his usual forms at prayers—he even prayed more than was his wont—but it was lip-service, and his soul took no part. This condition would sometimes last a day, or two days, and would then pass away. But these days were hideous. Kasatsky felt that he was neither in his own hands nor God's, but subject to some outside will. All he could do at those times was to follow the advice of his superior and undertake nothing, but simply wait.

On the whole, Kasatsky lived, then, not according to his own will, but in complete obedience to his superior; and in that obedience he found peace.

Such was Kasatsky's life in his first monastery, which lasted seven years. At the end of the third year he was ordained to the priesthood, and was given the name of Sergius. The ordination was a momentous event in his inner life. He had previously experienced great comfort and spiritual uplifting at holy communions. At first, when he was himself celebrating mass, at the moment of the oblation his soul was filled with exaltation. But gradually this sense became dulled ; and when on one occasion he had to celebrate mass in an hour of depression, as he sometimes had, he felt that this exaltation could not endure. The emotion eventually paled until only the habit was left.

On the whole, in the seven years of his life in the monastery Sergius began to grow weary. All that he had to learn, all that he had to attain, was done, and he had nothing more to do.

But his stupefaction only increased. During that time he heard of his mother's death and of Mary's marriage. Both events were matters of indifference to him, as all his attention and all his interest were concentrated on his inner life.

In the fourth year of his monastic experience, during which the bishop had shown him marked kindness, his superior told him that in the event of high honours being offered to him he should not decline. Just then monastic ambition—precisely that quality which was so disgusting to him in all the other monks—arose within him. He was sent to a monastery close to the capital. He would have been glad to refuse, but his superior ordered him to accept ; so he obeyed, and taking leave of his superior, left for the other monastery.

This transfer to the monastery near the metropolis was an important event in Sergius's life. There he encountered many temptations, and his whole will power was concentrated on the struggle they entailed. In the first monastery women were no trial to him, but in the second instance this special temptation assumed grave dimensions, and even took definite shape.

There was a lady known for her frivolous behaviour who began to seek his favour. She talked to him and asked him to call upon her. Sergius refused with severity, but was horrified at the definiteness of his desire. He was so alarmed that he wrote to his superior. Moreover, for the sake of humiliation, he called a young novice and, conquering his shame, confessed his weakness. He begged him to keep an eye on him, and not let him go anywhere but to service and to do penance.

Besides that, Sergius suffered severely on account of his great antipathy to the abbot of this monastery, a worldly man and clever in worldly ways, who was making a career for himself within the church. In spite of his most earnest endeavours Sergius could not overcome his dislike for him. He was submissive to him, but in his heart he criticized him unceasingly. At last, when he had been there nearly two years, his real sentiments burst forth.

On the feast of the Intercession of the Virgin the vesper service was being celebrated in the church proper. There were many visitors from the neighbourhood, and the service was conducted by the abbot himself. Father Sergius was standing in his usual place, and was praying ; that is to say, he was engaged in that inner combat which always occupied him during service, especially in this second monastery.

The conflict was caused by his irritation at the presence of all the fine folk, and especially the ladies. He tried not to notice what was going on around him. He could not help, however, seeing a soldier who, while conducting the better-dressed people, pushed the common crowd aside, nor noticing the ladies who pointed out the monks, often himself and another monk as well who was noted for his good looks. He tried to concentrate his mind, to see nothing but the light of the candles on the ikonostasis, the sacred images, and the priests. He tried to hear nothing but the prayers which were spoken and chanted, to feel nothing

but self-oblivion in the fulfilment of his duty.
This was a feeling he always experienced when
he listened to prayers and anticipated the word
in the prayers he had so often heard.

So he stood, crossing himself, prostrating himself, struggling with himself, now indulging in
quiet condemnation, and now giving himself up
to that obliteration of thought and feeling which
he voluntarily induced in himself.

When the treasurer, Father Nicodemus (also
a great stumbling-block in Father Sergius's way—
that Father Nicodemus !), whom he couldn't help
censuring for flattering and fawning on the abbot,
approached him, and saluting him with a low bow
that nearly bent him in two, said that the abbot
requested his presence behind the holy gates,
Father Sergius straightened his cassock, covered
his head, and went circumspectly through the
crowd.

"*Lise, regardes à droite—c'est lui,*" he heard a
woman's voice say.

"*Où, où?   Il n'est pas tellement beau!*"

He knew they were referring to him. As his
habit was when he was tempted, he repeated,
" Lead us not into temptation." Dropping his eyes
and bowing his head, he walked past the lectern
and the canons, who at that moment were passing
in front of the ikonostasis, and went behind the

holy gates by the north portal. According to custom, he crossed himself, bending double before the ikon. Then he raised his head and looked at the abbot, whom, together with some one standing beside him in brilliant array, he had already seen out of the corner of his eye.

The abbot stood against the wall in his vestments, taking his short fat hands from beneath his chasuble and folding them on his fat stomach. Fingering the braid on his chasuble, he smiled as he talked to a man wearing the uniform of a general in the Emperor's suite, with insignia and epaulettes, which Father Sergius at once recognized with his experienced military eye. This general was a former colonel in command of his regiment, who now evidently held a very high position. Father Sergius at once noticed that the abbot was fully aware of this, and was so pleased that his fat red face and his bald head gleamed with satisfaction. Father Sergius was grieved and disgusted, and all the more so when he heard from the abbot that he had only sent for him to satisfy the curiosity of the general, who wanted to see his famous "colleague," as he put it.

"I am so glad to see you in your angelic guise," said the general, holding out his hand. "I hope you have not forgotten your old comrade."

The whole thing—the abbot's red and smiling face above his white beard in evident approval of the general's words ; the well-scrubbed face of the general with his self-satisfied smile, the smell of wine from the general's breath, and the smell of cigars from his whiskers—made Sergius boil.

He bowed once more before the abbot, and said, " Your grace deigned to call me——" and he stopped, asking by the very expression of his face and eyes, " What for ? "

The Abbot said, " Yes, to meet the general."

" Your grace, I left the world to save myself from temptation," he said, pale and with quivering lips ; " why, then, do you expose me to it during prayers in the house of God ? "

" Go ! go ! " said the abbot, frowning and growing angry.

Next day Father Sergius asked forgiveness of the abbot and of the brethren for his pride. But at the same time, after a night spent in prayer, he decided that his only possible course was to leave this monastery ; so he wrote a letter to his superior imploring him to grant him leave to return to his monastery. He wrote that he felt his weakness, and the impossibility of struggling alone against temptation without his help. He did penance for his sin of pride. The next post brought him a letter from the superior, who wrote that the sole cause of all his trouble was pride. The old man explained to him that his fits of anger were due to the fact that in refusing all clerical honour he humiliated himself not for the sake of God, but for the sake of his pride—merely for the sake of saying to himself : " Now, am I not a splendid fellow not to desire anything ? " That was why he could not tolerate the abbot's action. " I have renounced everything for the glory of God, and here I am exhibited like a wild beast ! " " If you would just give up vanity for God's glory you would be able to bear it," wrote the old man ; " worldly pride is not yet dead in you. I have thought often of you, Sergius, my son. I have prayed also, and this is God's message with regard to you : Go on as you are, and submit."

At that moment tidings came that the recluse Hilary, a man of saintly life, had died in the hermitage. He had lived there for eighteen years. The abbot of that hermitage inquired whether there was not a brother who would take his place.

" Now with regard to that letter of yours," wrote the superior, " go to Father Païssy, of the T—— Monastery. I have written to him about you, and asked him to take you into Hilary's cell. I do not say you could replace Hilary, but you

want solitude to stifle your pride. And may God
bless you in your undertaking."

Sergius obeyed his superior, showed his letter
to the abbot, and asking his permission, gave up
his cell, handed all his belongings over to the
monastery, and departed for the hermitage at
T——.

The abbot of that hermitage, a former merchant, received Sergius calmly and quietly, and
left him alone in his cell. This cell was a cave
dug in a mountain, and Hilary was buried there.
In a niche at the back was Hilary's grave, and in
front was a place to sleep, a small table, and a
shelf with ikons and books. At the entrance
door, which could be closed, was another shelf.
Upon that shelf food was placed once a day by a
brother from the monastery.

So Father Sergius became a hermit.

III.

During the Carnival in Sergius's second year of
seclusion a merry company of rich people, ladies
and gentlemen, from the neighbouring town made
up a troika party after a meal of Carnival pan-

cakes and wine. The company was composed of two lawyers, a wealthy landowner, an officer, and four ladies. One of the ladies was the wife of the officer ; another was the wife of the landowner ; the third was his sister, a young girl ; the fourth was a *divorcée*, beautiful, rich, a little mad, whose ways gave rise to amazement and indignation in the town.

The night was fine, the roads smooth as a floor. They drove ten miles out of town, and then held a consultation as to whether they should turn back or go on.

"But where does this road lead?" asked Madame Makovkin, the beautiful *divorcée*.

"To T——, twelve miles farther on," said the lawyer who was having a flirtation with Madame Makovkin.

"And beyond?"

"Then to L——, past the monastery."

"Oh, the one where Father Sergius is?"

"Yes."

"The handsome hermit—Kasatsky?"

"Yes."

"Oh, *messieurs et mesdames!* let us go in and see Kasatsky. We can rest at T—— and have a bite."

"But we shan't get home to-night?"

"We'll just spend the night at Kasatsky's then."

"Of course. There is a hostelry at the monastery, and a very good one. When I was defending Makine I stopped there."

"No, I shall spend the night at Kasatsky's!"

"Even your great power, dear lady, could not make that possible."

"Not possible? I'll bet you!"

"Good! If you spend the night at Kasatsky's I'll pay you whatever you like."

"*A discrétion!*"

"And you the same, remember."

"Agreed! Let's start."

They gave the driver some wine, and they opened a basket of pies, cakes, and wines for themselves. The ladies drew their white furs round about them. The postilions broke into a dispute as to which should go ahead, and the younger one, turning sharply round, lifted his whip-handle high up and shouted at the horses. The bells tinkled, and the runners creaked beneath the sledge ; the sledge swayed and rocked a little. The outer horses trotted smoothly and briskly, with their tightly-bound tails under the gaily-decorated breech-bands. The slippery road faded away rapidly. The driver held the reins tightly.

The lawyer and the officer, who sat on the back seat, talked nonsense to Madame Makovkin's neighbour, and she herself, huddled in her furs, sat motionless and in thought.

"Eternally the same old things—the ugliness of it!—shiny red faces reeking with liquor and with tobacco, the same words, the same thoughts, for ever the same abomination. And they are all content and satisfied that it should be so. And thus they will go on till they die. But I can't—it bores me. I want something to happen that will upset and shatter the whole thing. We might at least be frozen to death, as they were at Saratov. What would these people do? How would they behave? Execrably, I suppose. Everybody would think of nothing but himself, and I no less than the rest. But I have beauty—that's something. They know it. Well, and that monk—I wonder if he really is indifferent to beauty. No; they all care for it, just like that cadet last autumn. And what a fool he was!"

"Ivan Nicolaievich," she said.

He answered, "Yes?"

"How old is he?"

"Who?"

"Why, Kasatsky."

"Over forty, I should think."

"Does he receive visitors? Does he see everybody?"

"Everybody, yes; but not always."

"Cover up my feet. Not that way—how clumsy you are! Yes, like that. But you needn't squeeze them."

Thus they came to the forest where the cell was.

She stepped out of the sledge and bade them drive on. They tried to dissuade her, but she grew irritable and commanded them to go on.

Father Sergius was now forty-nine years old. His life in solitude was very hard : not because of fasting and prayers—he endured those easily —but it was the inner struggle which he had not anticipated. There were two reasons for this struggle : his religious doubts and the temptations of desire. He thought these were two different fiends; but they were one and the same. When his doubts were gone lust was gone. But thinking these were two different devils, he fought them separately. They, however, always attacked him together.

"O my God! my God!" he cried, "why dost Thou not give me faith ? There is lust, of course ; but even St. Anthony and the rest had to fight that. But faith—they had that! There are moments and hours and days when I do not possess it. Why does the world exist with all its charm if it is sinful and we must renounce it? Why hast Thou created this temptation ? Temptation? But isn't this temptation to renounce the joys of the world and to prepare for the life beyond, where there is nothing and where there can be nothing?" Saying this to himself, he became horrified and filled with disgust at himself. "You vile thing! And you think of being a saint!" he said.

He rose to pray. But when he began praying he saw himself as he appeared at the monastery in his vestments and all his grandeur, and he shook his head.

"No, that is not so. It is a lie. I may deceive all the world, but not myself, and not God. I am insignificant; I am pitiable;" and he pushed back the skirts of his cassock, and gazed at his thin legs in their underclothing.

Then he dropped his robe again and began to repeat his prayers, making the sign of the cross and prostrating himself.

"Will that couch be my bier?" he read; and, as if a demon whispered to him, he heard: "The solitary couch is also the coffin."

"It is a lie!" and he saw in imagination the shoulders of a widow who had been his mistress. He shook himself and went on reading. After having read the precepts he took up the Gospels. He opened the book at a passage that he had often repeated and knew by heart.

"Lord, I believe. Help thou my unbelief."

He stifled the doubts that arose. Just as one replaces an object without disturbing its balance, he carefully put his faith back into its position while it trembled at its base, and stepped back cautiously so as neither to touch it nor upset it. He again pulled himself together and regained his peace of mind ; and repeating his childish prayer : "O Lord, take me, take me !" felt not only at ease, but glad and thrilled. He crossed himself and lay down to sleep on his narrow bench, putting his light summer garment under his head. He dropped off to sleep at once. In his light slumber he heard small tinkling bells. He did not know whether he was dreaming or waking. But a knock at the door aroused him. He sat up on his couch, not trusting his senses. The knock came again. Yes, it was nearer—it was at his own door—and after it came the sound of a woman's voice.

"My God ! is it true that the devil takes the form of a woman, as I have read in the lives of the saints ? Yes—it is a woman's voice ! So timid—so sweet—so tender !" And he spat to exorcise the devil. "No ! It was only imagination !" and he went to the corner where the lectern stood, and fell on his knees, his regular and habitual motion that of itself gave him comfort and pleasure. He bowed low, his hair falling forward on his face, and pressed his bare forehead to the damp, cold floor. There was a draught from the floor. He read a psalm which, as old Father Piman had told him, would ward off the assaults of the devil. His light, slender frame started up upon its strong limbs, and he meant to go on reading his prayers. But he did not read. He involuntarily inclined his head to listen. He wanted to hear more.

All was silent. From the corner of the roof the same regular drops fell into the tub below. Without was a mist, a fog, that swallowed up the snow. It was still, very still. There was a sudden rustle at the window, and a distinct voice, the same tender, timid voice, a voice that could only belong to a charming woman—

"Let me in, for Christ's sake."

All the blood rushed to his heart and settled there. He could not even sigh.

"May the Lord appear and His enemies be confounded."

"But I am not the devil!" He could not hear that the words were spoken by smiling lips. "I am not the devil. I am just a wicked woman that's lost her way, literally and figuratively." (She laughed.) "I am frozen, and I beg for shelter."

He put his face close to the window. The little ikon lamp was reflected in the glass. He put his hands up to his face and peered between them. Fog, mist, darkness, a tree, and—at the right—she herself, a woman in thick white furs, in a fur cap, with a lovely, lovely, gentle, frightened face, two inches away, leaning towards him. Their eyes met and they recognized each other—not because they had ever seen each other before. They had never met. But in the look they exchanged they felt—and he particularly—that they knew each other, that they understood.

After that glance which they exchanged how could he entertain any further doubt that this was the devil instead of just a sweet, timid, frightened woman ?

"Who are you ? Why have you come ?" he asked.

"Open the door, I say," she said with whimsical authority. "I tell you I've lost my way."

"But I am a monk—a hermit."

"Open that door all the same. Do you want me to freeze while you say your prayers ?"

"But how——"

"I won't eat you. Let me in, for God's sake ! I'm quite frozen."

She began to be really frightened, and spoke almost tearfully.

He stepped back into the room, looked at the ikon representing the Saviour with His crown of thorns—

"God help me—help me, O God!" he said, crossing himself and bowing low. Then he went to the door which opened into the little porch, and feeling for the latch, tried to unhook it. He heard steps outside. She was going from the window to the door.

"Oh!" he heard her exclaim, and he knew she had stepped into a puddle made by the dripping rain. His hands trembled, and he could not move the hook, which stuck a little.

"Well, can't you let me in? I'm quite soaked, and I'm frozen. You are only bent on saving your own soul while I freeze to death."

He jerked the door towards him in order to raise the latch, and then, unable to measure his movements, pushed it open with such violence that it struck her.

"Oh—pardon!" he said suddenly, reverting to his former tone with ladies.

She smiled, hearing that "pardon." "Oh, well, he's not so dreadful," she thought. "Never mind, it is you who must pardon me," she said, passing by him. "I would never have ventured, but such an extraordinary circumstance——"

"If you please," he said, making way for her.

3

He was struck by the fragrance of fine perfume that he had not smelt for many a long day.

She went through the porch into the chamber. He shut the outer door without latching it and passed into the room after her. Not only in his heart but involuntarily moving his lips he repeated unceasingly, "O Lord Jesus Christ, Son of God, have mercy on me, a sinner—have mercy on me, a sinner!"

"If you please," he said to her again.

She stood in the middle of the room, dripping, and examined him closely. Her eyes smiled.

"Forgive me for disturbing your solitude," she said, "but you must see what a position I am placed in. It all came about by our coming out for a drive from town. I made a wager that I would walk by myself from Vorobievka to town. But I lost my way. That's how I happened to find your cell." Her lies now began.

But his face confused her so that she could not proceed, so she stopped. She expected him to be quite different from the man she saw. He was not as handsome as she had imagined, but he was beautiful to her. His gray hair and beard, slightly curling, his fine, regular features, and his eyes like burning coals when he looked straight at her, impressed her profoundly. He saw that she was lying.

"Yes, very well," he said, looking at her and dropping his eyes. "Now I will go in there, and this place is at your disposal."

He took the burning lamp down from before the ikon, lit a candle, and making a low bow went out to the little niche on the other side of the partition, and she heard him begin to move something there.

"He is probably trying to shut himself up away from me," she thought, smiling. Taking off her white fur, she tried to remove her cap, but it caught in her hair and in the knitted shawl she was wearing underneath it. She had not got wet at all standing outside at the window. She said so only as a pretext to be admitted. But she had really stepped into a puddle at the door, and her left foot was wet to the ankle, and one shoe was full of water. She sat down on his bed, a bench only covered with a carpet, and began to take her shoes off. The little cell pleased her. It was about nine feet by twelve, and as clean as glass. There was nothing in it save the bench on which she sat, the book-shelf above it, and the lectern in the corner. On the door were nails where his fur coat and his cassock hung. Beside the lantern was the image of Christ with His crown of thorns, and the lamp. The room smelt strangely of oil and of earth. She liked everything, even that smell. Her wet feet were uncomfortable, the left one especially, and she took off her shoes and stockings, never ceasing to smile. She was happy not only in having achieved her object, but because she perceived that he was troubled by her presence. He, the charming, striking, strange, attractive man!

"Well, if he wasn't responsive, it doesn't matter," she said to herself. "Father Sergius! Father Sergius!—or what am I to call you?"

"What do you want?" answered a low voice.

"Please forgive me for disturbing your solitude, but really I couldn't help it. I would have fallen ill. And even now I don't know if I shan't. I'm quite wet and my feet are like ice."

"Pardon me," answered the quiet voice, "I cannot be of any assistance to you."

"I would not have come if I could have helped it. I shall only stop till dawn."

He did not answer. She heard him muttering something, probably his prayers.

"I hope you will not come in here," she said, smiling, "for I must undress to get dry."

He did not answer, continuing to read his prayers in a steady voice.

"That is a man," she thought, as she attempted to remove her wet shoe. She tugged at it in vain and felt like laughing. Almost inaudibly, she did laugh; then, knowing that he would hear, and would be moved by it, just as she wanted him to be, she laughed louder. The kind, cheerful, natural laughter did indeed affect him just as she had wished.

"I could love a man like that—such eyes, and his simple, noble face, passionate in spite of all the prayers it mutters! There's no fooling us women in that. The instant he put his face against the window - pane and saw me, he knew me and understood me. The glimmer of it was in his eyes and a seal was set upon it for ever. That instant he began to love me and to want me. Yes, he wants me," she said, finally getting off her shoe and fumbling at her stocking.

To remove those long stockings fastened with elastic she had to raise her skirts. She felt embarrassed and said, "Don't come in." But there was no answer from the other side, and she heard the same monotonous murmurs and movements.

"I suppose he's bowing down to the ground," she thought. "But that won't help him. He's thinking about me just as I'm thinking about him. He's thinking about these very feet of mine," she said, taking off the wet stockings and sitting up on the couch barefooted, with her hands clasped about her knees. She sat awhile like this, gazing pensively before her.

"It's a perfect desert here. Nobody would ever know——"

She got down, took her stockings over to the stove and hung them on the damper. It was such a quaint damper! She turned it, and then slipping quietly over to the couch she sat up there again with her feet upon it. There was absolute silence on the other side of the partition. She looked at the little watch hanging round her neck. Two o'clock. "My people will return about three." She had more than an hour before her.

"Well! am I going to sit here by myself the whole time? Nonsense! I don't like that. I'll call him at once.—Father Sergius! Father Sergius! Sergei Dimitrievich! Prince Kasatsky!"

No answer.

"I say! that's cruel. I wouldn't call you if I didn't need you. I'm ill. I don't know what's the matter," she said in a tone of suffering. "Oh! oh!" she groaned, falling back on the couch; and, strange to say, she really felt that she was getting faint, that everything ached, that she was trembling as if with fever.

"Here, listen! Help me! I don't know what's the matter with—oh! oh!"

She opened her dress, uncovering her breast, and raised her arms, bare to the elbows, above her head. "Oh, oh!"

All this time he stood on the other side of the door and prayed.

Having finished all the evening prayers, he stood motionless, fixing his eyes on the end of his nose, and praying in his heart he repeated with all his soul : " Lord Jesus Christ, Son of God, have mercy on me ! "

He had heard everything. He had heard how the silk rustled when she took off her dress, how she stepped on the floor with her bare feet. He heard how she rubbed her hands and feet. He felt himself getting weak, and thought he might be lost at any moment. That was why he prayed unceasingly. His feelings must have been somewhat like those of the hero in the fairy tale who had to go on and on without ever turning back. Sergius heard and felt that the danger was there just above his head, around him, and that the only way to escape it was not to look round on it for an instant. Then suddenly the desire to see her came upon him, and at that very instant she exclaimed, " Now this is monstrous ! I may die."

" Yes, I will come.—But I will go like that saint who laid one hand upon the adulteress but put the other upon burning coals."

But there were no burning coals. He looked round. The lamp ! The lamp !

He put a finger over the flame and frowned,

ready to endure. In the beginning it seemed to him that there was no sensation. But then of a sudden, before he had decided whether it hurt him or how much it hurt him, his face writhed, and he jerked his hand away, shaking it in the air.

"No, that I can't do."

"For God's sake, come to me! I am dying! Oh!"

"Must I be lost? No!—I'll come to you presently," he said opening the door. And without looking at her he passed through the room to the porch where he used to chop wood. He felt about to find the block and the axe which were leaning against the wall.

"Presently!" he said, and taking the axe in his right hand, he laid the forefinger of his left hand upon the block. He raised the axe and struck at the finger below the second joint. The finger flew off more lightly than wood, and bounding up, turned over on the edge of the block and then on to the floor. Sergius heard that sound before he realized the pain; but ere he could recover his senses he felt a burning pain and the warmth of the flowing blood. He hastily pressed the end of his cassock to the maimed finger, pressed it to his hip, and going back into her room stood before the woman.

"What do you want?" he asked her in a low voice.

She looked at his pale face with its trembling cheeks and felt ashamed. She jumped up, grasped her fur, and throwing it around her shoulders tucked herself up in it.

"I was in pain—I've taken cold—I—Father Sergius—I——"

He turned his eyes, which were shining with the quiet light of joy upon her, and said,—

"Dear sister, why have you desired to lose your immortal soul? Temptation must come into the world, but woe to him by whom temptation cometh. Pray that God may forgive us both."

She listened and looked at him. Suddenly she heard the sound of something dripping. She looked closely and saw that blood was dropping from his hand on to his cassock.

"What have you done to your hand?"

She remembered the sound she had heard, and seizing the little ikon lamp, ran out to the porch. There on the floor she saw the bloody finger.

She returned with her face paler than his, and wanted to say something. But he went silently to his little apartment and shut the door.

"Forgive me," she said. "How can I atone for my sin?"

"Go."

" Let me bind your wound."

" Go hence."

She dressed hurriedly and silently and sat in her furs, waiting.

The sound of little bells reached her from outside.

" Father Sergius, forgive me."

" Go.　God will forgive you."

" Father Sergius, I will change my life. Do not forsake me."

" Go."

" Forgive—and bless me ! "

" In the name of the Father and of the Son and of the Holy Ghost," she heard from behind the door.　" Go."

She sobbed and went out from the cell.

The lawyer came forward to meet her.

" Well," he said, " I see I have lost.　There's no help for it.　Where will you sit ? "

" I don't care."

She took a seat in the sledge and did not speak a word till they reached home.

A year later she entered a convent as a novice and led a life of severe discipline under the guidance of hermit R—— who wrote her letters at long intervals.

IV.

Another seven years Father Sergius lived as a hermit. In the beginning he accepted a great part of what people used to bring him—tea, sugar, white bread, milk, clothes, and wood.

But as time went on he led a life of ever greater austerity. Refusing anything that could be thought superfluous, he finally accepted nothing but rye bread once a week. All that was brought to him he gave to the poor who visited him.

His entire time was spent in his cell in prayer or in conversation with visitors, whose number continually increased.

Father Sergius appeared in church only three times a year, and when it was necessary he went out to fetch water and wood.

After the episode with Madame Makovkin, the change he effected in her life, and her taking the veil, the fame of Father Sergius increased. Visitors came in greater and greater numbers, and monks came to live in his neighbourhood. A church was built there, and a hostelry. Fame, as usual, exaggerated his feats. People came from a great distance and began bringing invalids to him in the belief that he could heal them.

His first cure happened in the eighth year of his seclusion. He actually healed a boy of fourteen brought to him by his mother, who insisted on Father Sergius putting his hand on the child's head. The idea had never occurred to him that he could heal the sick. He would have regarded such a thought as a great sin of pride.

But the mother who brought the boy never ceased imploring him on her knees.

"Why wouldn't he help her son when he healed other people?" she asked, and again besought him in the name of Christ.

When Father Sergius replied that only God could heal, she said she wanted him only to lay his hands on his head and pray.

Father Sergius refused and went back to his cell. But next morning—for this happened in the autumn and the nights were already cold—coming out of his cell to fetch water, he saw the same mother with her child, the same boy of fourteen, and heard the same petitions.

Father Sergius remembered the parable of the righteous judge, and, contrary to his first instinct that he must indubitably refuse, he began to pray, and prayed until a resolve formed itself in his soul. This decision was that he must accede to the woman's request, and that her faith was sufficient to save her child. As for him, Father

Sergius, he would be in that case but the worthless instrument chosen by God.

Returning to the mother, Father Sergius yielded to her request, put his hand on the boy's head, and prayed.

The mother left with her son. In a month the boy was cured, and the fame of the holy healing power of "Old Father Sergius," as he was called then, spread abroad. From that time not a week passed without sick people coming to Father Sergius.

Complying with the requests of some, he could not refuse the rest ; he laid his hands on them and prayed. Many were healed, and his fame became more and more widespread.

Having thus passed seven years in the monastery and many years in the hermitage, he looked now like an old man. He had a long gray beard and his hair had grown thin.

V.

Now Father Sergius had for weeks been haunted by one relentless thought, whether it was right for him to have acquiesced in a state of things not so much created by himself as by the archimandrite and the abbot.

This state of things had begun after the healing of the boy of fourteen. Since that time Sergius felt that each passing month, each week and each day, his inner life had somehow been destroyed and a merely external life had been substituted for it. It was as if he had been turned inside out. Sergius saw that he was a means of attracting visitors and patrons to the monastery, and that, therefore, the authorities of the monastery tried to arrange matters in such a way that he might be most profitable to them. For instance, he had no chance of doing any work. Everything was provided that he could require, and the only thing they asked was that he should not refuse his blessing to the visitors who came to seek it. For his convenience, days were appointed on which he should receive them. A reception room was arranged for men ; and a place was also enclosed by railings in order that the crowds of women who came to him should not overwhelm him—a place where he could bestow his blessing upon those who came.

When he was told that he was necessary to men, and that if he would follow the rule of Christ's love he could not refuse them when they desired to see him, and that his holding aloof from them would be cruel, he could not but agree.

But the more he gave himself up to such an

existence the more he felt his inner life transformed into an external one.   He felt the fount of living water drying up within him, and that everything he did now was performed more and more for man and less for God.   Whatever he did, whether admonishing or simply blessing, or praying for the sick, or giving advice on the conduct of life, or listening to expressions of gratitude from those he had helped or healed (as they say), or instructed or advised, he could not help feeling a certain pleasure when they expressed their gratitude to him.   Neither could he be indifferent to the results of his activity nor to his influence.   He now thought himself a shining light.   But the more he harboured that idea, the more he was conscious of the fact that the divine light of truth which had previously burned within him was flickering and dying.

"How much of what I do is done for God and how much for man?"   That was the question that tormented him.   Not that he could not find an answer to it, but he dared not give an answer. He felt deep down in his soul that the devil had somehow changed all his work for God into work for man.   Because just as it had formerly been hard for him to be torn from solitude, now solitude itself was hard.   He was often wearied with visitors, but in the bottom of his heart he enjoyed their presence and rejoiced in the praise which was heaped on him.

There came a time when he made up his mind to go away, to hide. He even thought out a plan. He got ready a peasant shirt and peasant trousers, a coat, and a cap. He explained that he wanted them to give to the poor; and he kept these clothes in his cell, thinking how he would one day put them on and cut his hair, and go away. First he would take a train and travel for about three hundred miles. Then he would get out and walk from village to village. He asked an old soldier how he tramped—if people gave alms, and whether they admitted wayfarers into their houses. The soldier told him where people were most charitable, and where they would take a wanderer in for the night; and Father Sergius decided to act on his advice. One night he even put on those clothes and was about to go. But he did not know which was best, to remain or to run away. For a time he was undecided. Then the state of indecision passed. He grew accustomed to the devil and yielded to him; and the peasant clothes only served to remind him of thoughts and feelings that were no more.

Crowds flocked to him increasingly from day to day, and he had less and less time for prayers and for renewing his spiritual strength. Sometimes, in his brighter moments, he thought he was like a place where a brook had once been. There had been a quiet stream of living water which flowed out of him and through him, he thought. That had been real life, the time when she had tempted him. He always thought with ecstasy of that night and of her who was now Mother Agnes. She had tasted of that pure water. Since then the water had hardly been given time to collect before those who were thirsty arrived in crowds, pushing one another aside, and they had trodden down the little brook until nothing but mud was left. So he thought in his clearer moments. But his ordinary state of mind was weariness and a sort of tenderness for himself because of that weariness.

It was spring, the eve of a festal day. Father Sergius celebrated vespers in the church in the cave. There were as many people as the place could hold—about twenty altogether. They all belonged to the better classes, rich merchants and such-like. Father Sergius admitted every one to his church, but a selection was made by the monk appointed to serve him and by a man on duty who was sent to the hermitage every day from the monastery. A crowd of about eighty pilgrims, chiefly women, stood outside, waiting for Father Sergius to come out and bless them. In that part of the service, when he went to the tomb of his predecessor to bless it, he felt faint, and staggered, and would have fallen had it not been for a merchant who stood behind him and for the monk who served as deacon who caught him.

"What is the matter with you, Father Sergius, dear Father Sergius? O God!" exclaimed a woman's voice, "he is as white as a sheet!"

But Father Sergius pulled himself together, and though still very pale, pushed aside the deacon and the merchant and resumed the prayers. Father Serafian, the deacon, and the acolytes and a lady, Sophia Ivanovna, who always lived close by the hermitage to attend on Father Sergius, begged him to bring the service to an end.

"No, there's nothing the matter," said Father Sergius, faintly smiling from beneath his moustache and continuing his prayers. "Ah, that is the way of saints," he thought.

"A holy man—an angel of God," he heard Sophia Ivanovna and the merchant who had supported him a moment before murmur.

He did not heed their entreaties, but went on with the service. Crowding one another as before, they all filed through narrow passages back into the little church where Father Sergius completed vespers, merely curtailing the service a little. Directly after this, having pronounced the benediction on those present, he sat down outside on a little bench beneath an elm tree at the entrance to the cave. He wanted to rest—to breathe fresh air; he felt the need of it. But the moment he appeared, a crowd of people rushed to him soliciting his blessing, his advice, and his help. In the crowd was a number of women, pilgrims going from one holy place to another, from one holy man to another, ever in ecstasy before each sanctuary and before each saint.

Father Sergius knew this common, cold, irreligious, unemotional type. As for the men in the crowd, they were for the most part retired soldiers, long unaccustomed to a settled life; and most of them were poor, drunken old men who tramped from monastery to monastery merely for a living. The dull peasantry also flocked there, men and women, with their selfish requirements, seeking healing or advice in their little daily interests: how their daughters should be married, or a shop hired, or land bought, or how a woman could atone for a child she had over-lain in sleep and killed, or for a child she had borne out of wedlock.

All this was an old story to Father Sergius and did not interest him. He knew he would hear nothing new from them. The spectacle of their faces could not arouse any religious emotion in him. But he liked to look at them as a crowd which was in need of his benediction and revered his words. This made him like the crowd, although he found them fatiguing and tiresome.

Father Serafian began to disperse the people, saying that Father Sergius was weary. But Father Sergius recollected the words of the Gospel : "Suffer the little children to come unto me and forbid them not," and, touched at his recollection of the passage, he permitted them to approach. He rose, walked to the little railing beyond which the crowd had gathered, and began to bless them ; but his answers to their questions were so faint that he was moved at hearing himself.

Despite his wish to receive them all, it was too much for him. Everything grew dark again before his eyes, and he staggered and grasped the railings. He felt the blood rushing to his head, and grew pale and then scarlet.

"I must leave the rest till to-morrow, I can do no more now," he said ; and pronouncing a general benediction, returned to the bench.

The merchant supported him again, and taking him by the arm, assisted him to be seated. Voices exclaimed in the crowd,—

"Father, dear father, don't forsake us. We are lost without you."

The merchant, having helped Father Sergius to the bench under the elm tree, took upon himself the duties of policeman and began energetically to disperse the crowd. It was true he spoke in a low voice so that Father Sergius could not overhear, but he spoke very decidedly and in an angry tone.

"Get away, get away, I say! He has blessed you. What else do you want? Get along, or you'll catch it. Move on there! Get along there, old woman, with your dirty rags. Go on! Where do you think *you're* going? I told you it was finished. To-morrow's coming, but to-day he's done, I tell you!"

"Dear father! I only want to look on his dear face with my own little eyes," said an old woman.

"Little eyes indeed! You don't get in here!"

Father Sergius noticed that the merchant was doing it rather too thoroughly, and spoke to his attendant, saying the crowd was not to be turned away. He knew perfectly well that the crowd would be dispersed all the same, and he desired to remain alone and rest, but he sent his attendant with the order merely to make an impression.

"Well—well—I'm not turning them away, I'm only talking to them," answered the merchant. "They'll drive the man to death. They have no

mercy. They're only thinking of themselves.
No, I say! Get away! To-morrow!" and he
drove them all away.

The merchant took all this trouble because he
loved order and liked to turn people away and
abuse them ; but more because he wanted to have
Father Sergius to himself. He was a widower and
had an only daughter, an invalid and unmarried.
He had brought her fourteen hundred miles to
Father Sergius to be healed. During the two
years of the girl's illness he had taken her to
various cures. First to the university clinic in
the principal town of the province, but this was
not of much use ; then to a peasant in the province of Samara, who did her a little good. Afterwards he took her to a doctor in Moscow and
paid him a huge fee ; but this did not help at all.
Then he was told that Father Sergius wrought
cures, so he brought her to him. Consequently,
when he had scattered the crowd, he approached
Father Sergius, and falling upon his knees without
any warning, he said in a loud voice,—

"Holy father! Bless my afflicted child and
heal her of her sufferings. I venture to pros-
trate myself at your holy feet," and he put
one hand on another, palms up, cup-wise. All
this he did as if it were something distinctly and
rigidly appointed by law and usage—as if it were

the sole and precise method by which a man should request the healing of his daughter. He did it with such conviction that even Sergius felt for the moment that that was just the right way. However, he bade him rise from his knees and tell him what the trouble was. The merchant said that his daughter, a girl of twenty-two, had fallen ill two years before, after the sudden death of her mother. She just said "Ah!" as he put it, and went out of her mind. He had brought her fourteen hundred miles, and she was waiting in the hostelry till Father Sergius could receive her. She never went out by day, being afraid of the sunlight, but only after dusk.

"Is she very weak?" asked Father Sergius.

"No, she has no special weakness; but she's rather stout, and the doctor says she's neurasthenic. If you will just let me fetch her, Father Sergius, I'll be back with her in a minute. Revive, O holy father, the heart of a parent, restore his line, and save my afflicted offspring with your prayers!" and the merchant fell down on his knees again, and bending sideways with his head over his palms, which appeared to hold little heaps of something, remained like a figure in stone. Father Sergius again told him to get up, and thinking once more how trying his work was, and how patiently he bore it in

spite of everything, sighed heavily. After a few
moments' silence, he said : "Well, bring her
to-night. I will pray over her. But now I am
weary," and he closed his eyes. "I will send
for you."

The merchant went away, stepping on tiptoe,
which made his boots creak still louder, and
Father Sergius remained alone.

Father Sergius's life was filled with Church
services and with visitors ; but this day was
particularly difficult. In the morning an important official had come to hold a long conference
with him. Then a lady came with her son. The
son was a young professor, an unbeliever, and
his mother, who was ardently religious and
devoted to Father Sergius, brought him to
Father Sergius that he might talk to him. The
talk was very trying. The young man evidently
did not wish to have a discussion with the monk,
and just agreed with him in everything, as with an
inferior. Father Sergius saw that the youth was
an infidel, but that he had nevertheless a clear and
tranquil conscience. The memory of the conversation was now unpleasant to him.

"Won't you eat something, Father Sergius ?"
asked the attendant.

"Very well—bring me something."

The attendant went to a little hut built ten

paces from the cave, and Father Sergius remained alone.

The time was long past when Father Sergius lived alone, doing everything for himself, and having but a holy wafer and bread for nourishment. He had been warned long ago that he had no right to be careless of his health, and he was given wholesome meals, although of Lenten quality. He did not eat much, but more than he had done ; and sometimes he even felt a pleasure in eating : the disgust and the sense of sin he had experienced before was gone.

He took some gruel, and had a cup of tea with half a roll of white bread. The attendant went away while he remained alone on the bench under the elm tree. It was a beautiful evening in May. The leaves of the birches, the aspens, the elms, the alder bushes, and the oaks were just beginning to blossom. The alder bushes behind the elms were still in full bloom. A nightingale was singing near at hand, and two or three more in the bushes down by the river trilled and warbled. From the river came the songs of working-men, perhaps on their way home from their labours. The sun was setting behind the forest and was throwing little broken rays of light among the leaves. This side was bright green and the other side was dark. Beetles were flying about, and

colliding together, were falling to the ground.
After supper Father Sergius began to repeat a
prayer mentally : "O Lord Jesus Christ, Son of
God, have mercy on us," and then he read
a psalm.

Suddenly, in the middle of the psalm, a sparrow
flew out from a bush on the ground, and hopping
along, came to him ; then it flew away, frightened.
He was reading a prayer that bore upon renunciation of the world, and hastened to get to the
end of it in order that he might send for the
merchant and his daughter. He was interested
in the daughter because she offered a sort of
diversion, and also because she and her father
thought him a saint—a saint whose prayer was
efficacious. He repudiated the idea, but in the
depths of his soul he nevertheless concurred.
He often wondered how he, Sergius Kasatsky,
had contrived to become such an extraordinary
saint and worker of miracles ; but that it was
a fact, he did not doubt. He could not fail
to believe in the miracles he saw with his own
eyes, beginning with the sick boy and ending
with this last old woman who had recovered
her sight through his prayers. Strange as it
was, it was a fact. Accordingly the merchant's
daughter interested him as a new individual that
had faith in him, and besides, as an occasion

of bearing witness to his healing power and to
his fame.

"People come thousands of miles. Papers
talk about it. The Emperor knows. All Europe
knows—all godless Europe;" and then he felt
ashamed of his vanity and began to pray.

"God, King of heaven, Comforter, True Soul,
come into—inspire me—and cleanse me from all
sin, and save, O All-merciful, my soul. Cleanse
me from the sin of worldly vanity that has over-
taken me," he said, remembering how often
he had made that prayer and how vain it had
been. His prayers worked miracles for others,
but as for himself God had not granted him
strength to conquer this petty passion. He remembered his prayers at the commencement of
his seclusion, when he asked for the grace of
purity, humility, and love, and how it seemed to
him at that time that God heard his prayers.
He had retained his purity and had hewn off
his finger. He raised the stump of the finger
with folds of skin on it to his lips and kissed
it. It seemed to him now that at that time,
when he had been filled with disgust at his own
sinfulness, he had been humble, and that he
had also possessed love. He recalled also the
tender feelings with which he had received the
old drunken soldier who had come to ask alms

of him ; and how he had received *her*. And now ? He asked himself whether he loved anybody ; whether he loved Sophia Ivanovna or Father Serafian ; whether he had any feeling of love for those who had come to him that day. He asked himself if he had felt any love towards the learned young man with whom he had held that instructive discussion with the object only of showing off his own intelligence and proving that he had not fallen behind in knowledge.

He wanted love from them, and rejoiced in it, but felt no love himself for them. Now he had neither love nor humility. He was pleased to hear that the merchant's daughter was twenty-two, and was anxious to know if she was good-looking. When he inquired if she was weak, he only wanted to know if she had feminine charm. " Is it true that I have fallen so low ?" he thought. " God help me ! Restore my strength—restore me, O God my Saviour ! " and he clasped his hands and began to pray.

The nightingales sang, a beetle flew at him and crept along the back of his neck. He brushed it away.

" But does He exist ? What if I am knocking at a house which is locked from without. The bar is on the door, and we can see it. Nightingales, beetles, nature, are the bar to our understanding.

That young man was perhaps right." He began
to pray aloud, and prayed long, till all these
thoughts disappeared and he became calm and
firm in the faith. He rang the bell, and told the
attendant to say that the merchant might now
come with his daughter.

The merchant came, leading his daughter by
the arm, and brought her to the cell, where he
left her.

The daughter was pale, with fair hair. She
was very short, and had a frightened, childish
face and full figure. Father Sergius remained
seated on the bench at the entrance. When the
girl passed him and stood near him he blessed
her, feeling aghast because of the way in which
he looked at her figure. As she passed by him
he felt a sting. He saw by her face that she was
sensual and feeble-minded. He rose and entered
his cell. She was sitting on a stool waiting for
him, and when he entered she rose.

"I want to go back to my papa," she said.

"Do not be afraid," he said. "Where do you
feel pain?"

"I feel pain all over," she answered, and
suddenly her face brightened with a smile.

"You will regain your health," he said. "Pray."

"What's the use? I've prayed. It doesn't
help," and she continued smiling. "I wish you

would pray and lay your hands on me. I saw you in a dream."

" How so ? "

" I saw you put your hand on my chest.'

She took his hand and pressed it to her breast.

" Here."

He yielded his right hand to her.

" What is your name ? " he asked, his whole body shaking, and feeling that he was overcome and could not control his instinct.

" Marie.   Why ? "

She took his hand and kissed it, and then put her arm round his waist and pressed him.

" Marie, what are you doing ? " he said.   " You are a devil, Marie ! "

" Oh, perhaps.   Never mind."

And embracing him, she sat down at his side on the bed.

At dawn he went out of the door.   Had all this really happened ?   Her father would come. She would tell.   " She's a devil.   But what have *I* done ?   Oh, there is the axe which I used to chop off my finger."

He took the axe and went back to the cell.

The attendant came towards him.   " Do you want some wood cut ?   Give me the axe."

He gave him the axe, and entered the cell. She lay asleep. He looked on her with horror. Going back into the cell he put on the peasant clothes, seized the scissors, cut his hair, and then, issuing forth, took the path down the hill to the river, where he had not been for four years.

The road ran along the river. He went by it, walking till noon. Then he went into a cornfield and lay among the corn. Towards evening he approached a village, but did not enter it. He went again to the river, to a cliff.

It was early morning, half an hour before sunrise. All was gray and mournful around him, and a cold, early morning wind blew from the west.

"I must end it all. There is no God. How can I do it? Throw myself in! I can swim; I should not drown. Hang myself? Yes; just with this belt, to a branch."

This seemed so feasible and so easy that he wanted to pray, as he always did in moments of distress. But there was nothing to pray to. God was not. He dropped down on his elbow, and such a longing for sleep instantly overcame him that he couldn't hold his head up with his arm any longer. Stretching out his arm, he laid his head upon it and went to sleep. But this sleep lasted only a moment. He awoke at once, and what followed was half dream and half recollection.

He saw himself as a child in the house of his mother in the country. A carriage was approaching, and out of it stepped Uncle Nicholas Sergeivich, with a long black beard like a spade, and with him a slender girl, Pashinka, with large soft eyes and a timid, pathetic little face. This girl was taken to the place where the boys were playing, and they were forced to play with her, which was very tedious indeed. She was a silly little girl, and it ended in their making fun of her, and making her show them how she swam. She lay down on the floor and went through the motions. They laughed and turned her into ridicule; which, when she became aware of it, made her blush in patches. She looked so piteous that his conscience pricked him, and he could never forget her kind, submissive, tremulous smile. Sergius remembered how he had seen her since then. A long time ago, just before he became a monk, she had married a landowner, who had squandered all her fortune, and who beat her. She had two children, a son and a daughter. The son died when he was little, and Sergius remembered seeing her, very wretched, after that; and then again at the monastery, when she was a widow. She was still just the same; not exactly stupid, but insipid, insignificant, and piteous. She had come with her daughter and her daughter's *fiancé*. They were poor at that time, and later on he heard that she was living in a little provincial town and was almost destitute.

"Why does she come into my head?" he asked himself; but still he could not help thinking about her. "Where is she? What has become of her? Is she as unhappy as she was when she had to show us how she swam on the floor? But what's the use of my thinking of her now? My business is to put an end to myself."

Again he was afraid, and again, in order to spare himself, he began to think about her. Thus he lay a long time, thinking now of his extraordinary end, now of Pashinka. She seemed somehow the means of his salvation. At last he fell asleep, and in his dream he saw an angel, who came to him and said,—

"Go to Pashinka. Find out what you have to do, and what your sin is, and what is your way of salvation."

He awoke, convinced that this was a vision from on high. He rejoiced, and resolved to do as he was told in the dream. He knew the town where she lived, three hundred miles away, so he walked to that place.

4

VI.

Pashinka was no longer Pashinka. She had become Praskovia Mikhailovna, old, wrinkled, and shrivelled, the mother-in-law of a drunken official, Mavrikiev—a failure. She lived in the little provincial town where he had occupied his last position, and had supported the family : a daughter, a nervous, ailing husband, and five grandchildren. Her sole means of supporting them was by giving music lessons to the daughters of merchants for fifty kopeks an hour. She had sometimes four, sometimes five, lessons a day, and earned about sixty roubles a month. They all lived for the moment on that in expectation of another situation. She had sent letters to all her friends and relations, asking for a post for her son-in-law, and had also written to Sergius ; but the letter had never reached him.

It was Saturday, and Praskovia Mikhailovna was kneading dough for currant bread such as the cook, a serf on her father's estate, used to make, for she wanted to give her grandchildren a treat on Sunday.

Her daughter Masha was looking after her youngest child, and the eldest boy and girl were at school. As for her husband, he had not slept that night, and was now asleep. Praskovia Mikhailovna had not slept well either, trying to appease her daughter's anger against her husband.

She saw that her son-in-law, being a weak character, could not talk or act differently, and she perceived that the reproaches of his wife availed nothing. All her energies were employed in softening these reproaches. She did not want harsh feelings and resentment to exist. Physically she could not stand a condition of ill-will. It was clear to her that bitter feelings did not mend matters, but simply make them worse. She did not think about it. Seeing anger made her suffer precisely as a bad odour or a shrill sound or a blow.

She was just showing Lucaria, the servant, how to mix the dough when her grandson Misha, a boy six years old, with little crooked legs in darned stockings, ran into the kitchen looking frightened.

"Grandmother, a dreadful old man wants to see you!"

Lucaria looked out of the door.

"Oh, ma'am, it's a pilgrim."

Praskovia Mikhailovna wiped her thin elbows with her hands, and then her hands on her apron, and was about to go into the room to get five kopeks out of her purse, when she remembered that she had only a ten-kopek piece, so, deciding to give bread instead, she turned to the cupboard. But then she blushed at the thought of having grudged him alms, and ordering Lucaria to cut a slice of bread, went to fetch the ten kopeks. "That serves you right," she said to herself. "Now you must give twice as much."

She gave both bread and money to the pilgrim with apologies, and in doing so she was not at all proud of her generosity. On the contrary, she was ashamed of having given so little, the man had such an imposing appearance.

In spite of having tramped three hundred miles, begging in the name of Christ, and being nearly in rags—in spite of having grown thin and weather-beaten, and having his hair cut, and wearing a peasant cap and boots—in spite, also, of his bowing with great humility—Sergius had the same impressive appearance which had attracted every one to him. Praskovia Mikhailovna did not recognize him. How could she, not having seen him for many years ?

"Excuse this humble gift, father. Wouldn't you like something to eat ? "

He took the bread and money, and Praskovia Mikhailovna was astonished that he did not go, but stood looking at her.

"Pashinka, I have come to you. Won't you take me in ? "

His beautiful black eyes looked at her intently, imploringly, and shone, tears starting; and his lips quivered painfully under the gray moustache.

Praskovia Mikhailovna pressed her hand to her shrivelled breast, opened her mouth, and stared at the pilgrim with dilated eyes.

"It can't be possible! Steph—Sergius—Father Sergius!"

"Yes, it is I," said Sergius in a low voice. "But no longer Sergius or Father Sergius, but a great sinner, Stephen Kasatsky—a great sinner, a lost sinner. Take me in—help me."

"No, it can't be possible! Such great humility! Come." She stretched out her hand; but he did not take it, he only followed her.

But where could she lead him? They had very little space. She had a tiny little room for herself, hardly more than a closet; but even that she had given up to her daughter, and now Masha was sitting there rocking the baby to sleep.

"Please be seated here," she said to Sergius, pointing to a bench in the kitchen.

He sat down at once, and took off, with an evidently accustomed action, the straps of his wallet first from one shoulder and then from the other.

"Heavens! what humility! what an honour! And now——"

Sergius did not answer, but smiled meekly, laying his wallet on one side.

"Masha, do you know who this is?" And Praskovia Mikhailovna told her daughter in a whisper. They took the bed and the cradle out of the little room, and made it ready for Sergius.

Praskovia Mikhailovna led him in.

"Now have a rest. Excuse this humble room. I must go."

"Where?"

"I have lessons. I'm ashamed to say I teach music."

"Music! That is well. But just one thing, Praskovia Mikhailovna. I came to you with an object. Could I have a talk with you?"

"I shall be happy. Will this evening do?"

"It will. One thing more. Do not say who I am. I have only revealed myself to you. No one knows where I went, and no one need know."

"Oh, but I told my daughter——"

"Well, ask her not to tell any one."

Sergius took off his boots and slept after a sleepless night and a forty-mile tramp.

When Praskovia Mikhailovna returned Sergius was sitting in the little room waiting for her. He had not come out for dinner, but had some soup and gruel which Lucaria brought in to him.

"Why did you return earlier than you said?" asked Father Sergius. "May I speak to you now?"

"What have I done to deserve the happiness of having such a guest! I only missed one lesson. That can wait. I have dreamed for a long time of going to see you. I wrote to you. And now this good fortune!"

"Pashinka, please listen to what I am going to tell you, as if it were a confession—as if it were something I should say to God in the hour of death. Pashinka, I am not a holy man; I am a vile and loathsome sinner. I have gone astray through pride, and I am the vilest of the vile."

Pashinka stared at him. She believed what he said. Then, when she had quite taken it in, she touched his hand and smiled sadly, and said,—

"Stevie, perhaps you exaggerate."

"No, Pashinka. I am an adulterer, a murderer, a blasphemer, a cheat."

"My God, what does he mean?" she muttered.

"But I must go on living. I, who thought I knew everything, who taught others how to live, I know nothing. I ask you to teach me."

"O Stevie, you are laughing at me. Why do you always laugh at me?"

"Very well; have it as you will that I am

laughing at you.   Still, tell me how you live, and how you have lived your life."

"I?   But I've lived a very bad life—the worst life possible.   Now God is punishing me, and I deserve it.   And I am so miserable now—so miserable!"

"And your marriage—how did you get on?"

"It was all bad.   I married because I fell in love from low motives.   Father didn't want me to, but I wouldn't listen to anything.   I just married.   And then, instead of helping my husband, I made him wretched by my jealousy, which I couldn't overcome."

"He drank, I heard."

"Well, but I didn't give him any peace.   I reproached him.   That's a disease.   He couldn't stop it.   I remember now how I took his drink away from him.   We had such frightful scenes!" She looked at Kasatsky with pain in her beautiful eyes at the recollection.

Kasatsky called to mind that he had been told that her husband beat Pashinka, and looking at her thin withered neck with veins standing out behind her ears, the thin coil of hair, half gray, half auburn, he saw it all just as it happened.

"Then I was left alone with two children, and with no means."

"But you had an estate!"

"Oh, that was sold when Vasily was alive. And the money was—spent ; we had to live. And I didn't know how to work—like all the young ladies of that time. I was worse than the rest—quite helpless. So we spent everything we had. I taught the children. Masha had learnt something. Then Misha fell ill when he was in the fourth class in the school, and God took him. Masha fell in love with Vania, my son-in-law. He's a good man, but very unfortunate. He's ill."

"Mother," interrupted her daughter, "take Misha. I can't be everywhere."

Praskovia Mikhailovna started, rose, and stepping quickly in her worn shoes, went out of the room and came back with a boy of two in her arms. The child was throwing himself backwards and grabbing at her shawl.

"Where was I ? Yes—he had a very good post here, and such a good chief, too. But poor Vania couldn't go on, and he had to give up his position."

"What is the matter with him ?"

"Neurasthenia. It's such a horrid illness. We have been to the doctor, but he ought to go away, and we can't afford it. Still, I hope it will pass. He doesn't suffer much pain, but——"

"Lucaria !" said a feeble and angry voice. "She's always sent out when I need her. Mother !"

4 a

"I'm coming," said Praskovia Mikhailovna, again interrupting her conversation. "You see, he hasn't had his dinner yet. He can't eat with us."

She went out and arranged something, and came back, wiping her thin, dark hands.

"Well, this is the way I live. I complain, and I'm not satisfied, but, thank God, all my grandchildren are such nice healthy children, and life is quite bearable. But why am I talking about myself?"

"What do you live on?"

"Why, I earn a little. How I used to hate music! and now it's so useful to me."

Her small hand lay on the chest of drawers that stood beside her where she was sitting, and she drummed exercises with her thin fingers.

"How much are you paid for your lessons?"

"Sometimes a rouble, sometimes fifty kopeks, and sometimes thirty. They are all so kind to me."

"And do your pupils get on well?" asked Kasatsky, smiling faintly with his eyes.

Praskovia Mikhailovna did not believe at first that he was asking her seriously, and looked inquiringly into his eyes.

"Some of them do," she said. "I have one very nice pupil, the butcher's daughter—such a good, kind girl. If I were a clever woman I could surely use my father's influence and get a position

for my son-in-law.   But it is my fault they are so
badly off.   I brought them to it."

"Yes, yes," said Kasatsky, dropping his head.
"Well, Pashinka, and what about your attitude to
the Church."

"Oh, don't speak of it!   I'm so bad that way.
I have neglected it so!   When the children have
to go, I fast and go to communion with them, but
as for the rest of the time I often do not go for a
month.   I just send them."

"And why don't you go?"

"Well, to tell the truth"—she blushed—"I'm
ashamed for Masha's sake and the children's to go
in my old clothes.   And I haven't anything else.
Besides, I'm just lazy."

"And do you pray at home?"

"I do; but it's just a mechanical sort of praying.
I know it's wrong.   But I have no real religious
feeling.   I only know I'm wicked—that's all."

"Yes, yes.   That's right, that's right!" said
Kasatsky, as if in approval.

"I'm coming—I'm coming!" she called, in
answer to her son-in-law, and tidying her hair,
went to the other room.

This time she was absent a long while.   When
she returned, Kasatsky was sitting in the same
position, his elbow on his knee and his head down.
But his wallet was ready strapped on his back.

When she came in with a little tin lamp without a shade, he raised his beautiful, weary eyes and sighed deeply.

"I didn't tell them who you were," she began shyly. "I just said you were a pilgrim—a nobleman—and that I used to know you. Won't you come into the dining-room and have tea?"

"No."

"Then I'll bring some in to you here."

"No; I don't want anything. God bless you, Pashinka. I am going now. If you have any pity for me, don't tell any one you have seen me. For the love of God, tell no one. I thank you. I would kneel down before you, but I know it would only make you feel awkward. Forgive me, for Christ's sake!"

"Give me your blessing."

"God bless you. Forgive me, for Christ's sake!"

He rose to go, but she restrained him, and brought him some bread and butter, which he took, and departed.

It was dark, and he had hardly passed the second house when he was lost to sight, and she only knew he was there because the dog at the priest's house was barking.

"That was the meaning of my vision. Pashinka

is what I should have been, and was not. I lived
for man, on the pretext of living for God; and
she lives for God, imagining she lives for man!
Yes; one good deed—a cup of cold water given
without expectation of reward—is worth far more
than all the benefits I thought I was bestowing
on the world. But was there not, after all, one
grain of sincere desire to serve God?" he asked
himself. And the answer came: " Yes, there was;
but it was so soiled, so overgrown with desire for
the world's praise. No; there is no God for the
man who lives for the praise of the world. I must
now seek *Him*."

He walked on, just as he had made his way
to Pashinka, from village to village, meeting and
parting with other pilgrims, and asking for bread
and a night's rest in the name of Christ. Sometimes an angry housekeeper would abuse him,
sometimes a drunken peasant would revile him;
but for the most part he was given food and
drink, and often something to take with him.
Many were favourably disposed towards him on
account of his noble bearing. Some, on the other
hand, seemed to enjoy the sight of a gentleman so
reduced to poverty. But his gentleness vanquished
all hearts.

He often found a Bible in a house where he
was staying. He would read it aloud, and the

people always listened to him, touched by what he read them, and wondering, as if it were something new, although so familiar.

If he succeeded in helping people by his advice, or by knowing how to read and write, or by settling a dispute, he did not afterwards wait to see their gratitude, for he went away directly. And little by little God began to reveal Himself within him.

One day he was walking along the road with two women and a soldier. They were stopped by a party consisting of a lady and gentleman in a trap drawn by a trotter, and another gentleman and lady riding. The gentleman beside the lady in the trap was evidently a traveller—a Frenchman —while her husband was on horseback with his daughter.

The party stopped to show the Frenchman the pilgrims, who, according to a superstition of the Russian peasantry, show their superiority by tramping instead of working. They spoke French, thinking they would not be understood.

" *Demandez-leur*," asked the Frenchman, " *s'ils sont bien sûres de ce que leur pèlerinage est agréable à Dieu ?* " they were asked.

The old woman answered,—

" Just as God wills it. Our feet have arrived at the holy places, but we can't tell about our hearts."

They asked the soldier. He answered that he was alone in the world, and belonged to nowhere.

They asked Kasatsky who he was.

" A servant of God."

" *Qu'est-ce qu'il dit? Il ne répond pas?*"

" *Il dit qu'il est un serviteur de Dieu.*"

" *Il doit être un fils de prêtre. Il a de la race. Avez-vous de la petite monnaie?*"

The Frenchman had some change, and gave each of them twenty kopeks.

" *Mais dites-leur que ce n'est pas pour les cierges que je leur donne, mais pour qu'ils se régalent du thé.* Tea—tea," he said, with a smile. " *Pour vous, mon vieux.*" And he patted Kasatsky on the shoulder with his gloved hand.

" Christ save you," said Kasatsky, and without putting on his hat, bent his bald head.

Kasatsky rejoiced particularly in this incident, because he had shown contempt for the world's opinion, and had done something quite trifling and easy. He accepted twenty kopeks, and gave them afterwards to a blind beggar who was a friend of his.

The less he cared for the opinion of the world the more he felt that God was with him.

For eight months Kasatsky tramped in this fashion, until at last he was arrested in a provincial town in a night-shelter where he passed the night with other pilgrims. Having no passport to show, he was taken to the police-station. When he was asked for documents to prove his identity he said he had none—that he was a servant of God. He was numbered among the tramps and sent to Siberia.

There he settled down on the estate of a rich peasant, where he still lives. He works in the vegetable garden, teaches the children to read and write, and nurses the sick.

THE LIGHT THAT SHINES IN DARKNESS.

DRAMATIS PERSONÆ.

Nicholas Ivanovich Sarintsev.

Marie Ivanovna (Masha), his wife.

Luba (Lubov Nicolaevna),
Missie,
Katia,
} their daughters.

Stephen,
Vania,
} their sons.

Mitrofan Dmitrich. Tutor to Vania.

Alexandra Ivanovna. Sister to Marie Ivanovna.

Peter Semenovich Kokhovtsev. Her husband.

Lisa. Their daughter.

Princess Cheremshanova.

Boris. Her son.

Tonia. Her daughter.

Father Vasily (Vasily Ermilovich). A village
priest.

Father Gerasim.

Alexis Mikhailovich Starkovsky.

Nurse and Footmen in Sarintsev's house.

Ivan,
Sebastian,
Ephraim,
Peter,
} Peasants.

A Peasant Woman. Ivan's wife.

Malashka. Ivan's daughter.

Alexander Petrovich. A tramp.

A country Police Sergeant.

Lawyer.

Yakov. Carpenter.

Clerk.

Sentries.

General.

Colonel.

Aide-de-camp.

Soldiers.

Police Officer.

Stenographer.

Chaplain.

Patients in Hospital.

Sick Officer.

Head Physician.

House Surgeon.

Warders.

Countess and other Guests at Sarintsev's dance.

Pianist.

ACT I.

The stage represents a covered veranda in a rich country-house. In front of the veranda are a flower garden, a tennis-court, and a croquet-lawn. The children with their governess are playing croquet. On the veranda are seated Marie Ivanovna Sarintsev, *a handsome, elegant woman of forty; her sister,* Alexandra Ivanovna Kokhovtsev, *a fat, positive, and stupid woman of forty-five; and her husband,* Peter Semenovich Kokhovtsev, *a fat, stout, clumsy man of slovenly appearance, wearing a summer suit and eye-glasses. They all sit at a table laid for breakfast with samovar and coffee. All are drinking coffee;* Peter Semenovich *is smoking.*

Alexandra.

If you were not my sister, and Nicholas Ivanovich were not your husband, but merely an acquaintance, I should find all this novel and charming, and should perhaps uphold him. I should have found it very nice. But when I see your husband playing the fool, simply playing the fool, I cannot help telling you what I think of it. And I shall tell him too, that husband of yours. I shall speak straight out to dear Nicholas. I am not afraid of anybody.

Marie.

I do not mind in the least: I see it myself. But I really do not think it is as important as all that.

Alexandra.

You may not think so ; but I assure you, if you let it go on, you will all be beggared. That is what will come of this sort of thing. . .

Peter.

Beggared, indeed ! With their fortune !

Alexandra.

Yes, beggared. Don't interrupt me. Of course, you always think that anything a man does is right.

Peter.

I don't know. I only say. . . .

Alexandra.

You never know what you are talking about, and when once you men begin your nonsense, there is no knowing where it will end. All I say is, that if I were in your place, I should not allow it. I should have put a stop to all this. I never heard of such a thing. The husband, the head of the family, does nothing, neglects his affairs, gives everything away, and plays the bountiful right and left. I know how it will end. I know all about it.

PETER

(*to* MARIE IVANOVNA). Do explain to me, Marie, what this new fad of his is. There are Liberals, County Councils, the Constitution Schools, reading-rooms, and all the rest of it—I understand all that. Then there are Socialists, strikes, an eight-hour day—I understand that too. But what is all this? Do explain.

MARIE.

He told you all about it yesterday.

PETER.

I own that I could not understand. The Gospel, the Sermon on the Mount, that churches are unnecessary. But where are we to pray, and all that?

MARIE.

That is the worst of it. He would destroy everything and put nothing in its place.

PETER.

How did it begin?

MARIE.

It began last year, when his sister died. He became very gloomy, perpetually spoke of death, and then fell ill, as you know. And after his typhoid fever he changed entirely.

ALEXANDRA.

Still he came to see us in Moscow in the spring, and he was very amiable and played cards. He was very nice and quite normal.

MARIE.

Yes, but he was not the same.

PETER.

In what way ?

MARIE.

He was perfectly indifferent to his family, and the New Testament had become an obsession. He read it all day ; at night he got up to read it instead of sleeping, making notes and copying out passages. Then he began to visit bishops and aged monks to discuss religion.

ALEXANDRA.

Did he go to confession and take the sacrament ?

MARIE.

Before that he had not done so since his marriage, that is for twenty-five years. But at the time I am speaking of he confessed and took communion at the monastery, and immediately afterwards decided it was unnecessary to confess, or even to go to church at all.

ALEXANDRA.

You see how inconsistent he is. A month ago he went to church and kept all the fasts; now suddenly he thinks all that is useless.

MARIE.

Well, talk to him yourself.

ALEXANDRA.

I will ; indeed I will.

PETER.

All that does not matter much.

ALEXANDRA.

It seems to you that it does not matter, because men have no religion.

PETER.

Do let me speak. I say that that is not the point. If he denies the Church, where does the New Testament come in ?

MARIE.

He says we are to live in accordance with the Sermon on the Mount, and give everything away.

PETER.

How are we to live ourselves if we give everything away?

ALEXANDRA.

And where does the Sermon on the Mount
order us to shake hands with our footmen? It
says, "Blessed are the meek," but there is not a
word about shaking hands.

MARIE.

Of course he is fanatical in this, as he always
is when he takes up anything. At one time it
was music, then schools. . . . But that does not
make it any easier for me.

PETER.

Why has he gone to town?

MARIE.

He did not tell me, but I know he has gone
to attend the hearing of the timber-stealing case.
The peasants cut down some of our forest.

PETER.

Those big fir trees?

MARIE.

Yes. They were condemned to pay for them,
and sentenced to imprisonment, and their appeal

is to be heard to-day. I am sure that is why he went.

ALEXANDRA.

He will forgive them, and to-morrow they will come and chop down all the trees in his park.

MARIE.

They seem to be beginning already. All the apple trees are broken, and the fields trampled. He forgives it all.

PETER.

How extraordinary !

ALEXANDRA.

That is exactly why I say that you must interfere. If it continues much longer—everything will go. I think it is your duty as a mother to take some steps.

MARIE.

What can I do ?

ALEXANDRA.

What can you do, indeed ? Put a stop to it, make him understand that it is impossible. You have children.   What an example to set them !

MARIE.

It is hard, but I try to bear it, and to hope that

this will pass as all his other infatuations have done.

ALEXANDRA.

Yes ; but God helps those who help themselves. You must make him feel that he is not alone, and that he is not living in the proper way.

MARIE.

The worst of it all is that he takes no interest in the children. I have to settle everything by myself. On the one hand I have a baby, and on the other, grown-up children—a girl and a boy—who both need attention and guidance, and I am alone. He used to be such a careful and tender father. Now he does not care about anything. Last night I told him Vania was lazy and had failed again in his examinations, and he said it would be much better for him to leave school altogether.

PETER.

Where would he send him ?

MARIE.

Nowhere. That is the horrible part of it. Everything is wrong, but he does not say what we are to do.

PETER.

How strange !

ALEXANDRA.

Not at all strange. It is just the usual way you men have of finding fault with everything, and doing nothing yourselves.

MARIE.

Stephen has finished his studies and must decide what he is going to do, but his father will not say anything to him about it. He wanted to enter the Civil Service—his father said it was useless; he wanted to enter the Horse Guards—Nicholas Ivanovich disapproved. The boy asked what he was to do, and his father asked why he did not go and plough : that would be far better than the Civil Service. What is he to do? He comes to me for advice, and I have to decide. But the means of carrying out any plan are in his father's hands.

ALEXANDRA.

You ought to tell Nicholas so plainly.

MARIE.

Yes ; I must talk to him.

ALEXANDRA.

Tell him plainly that you cannot stand it ; that you do your duty and that he must do his. Otherwise, he had better make the property over to you.

MARIE.

Oh ! that is so unpleasant.

ALEXANDRA.

I will tell him, if you like.   I will tell him so straight out.

> (*A young* PRIEST *enters, somewhat shy and nervous.   He carries a book and shakes hands with all present.*)

FATHER VASILY.

I have come to see Nicholas Ivanovich.   I've —I've brought back a book.

MARIE.

He has gone to town, but he will soon return.

ALEXANDRA.

What book did he lend you ?

FATHER VASILY.

It is Renan—yes—a book—the Life of Jesus.

PETER.

Oh ! what a book for you to read.

ALEXANDRA

(*contemptuously*).   Did Nicholas Ivanovich give you that to read ?   Well, do you agree with Nicholas Ivanovich and with Monsieur Renan ?

FATHER VASILY

(*excited, lighting a cigarette*). Yes, Nicholas Ivanovich gave it to me to read. Of course I do not agree with it. If I did I should not be, so to speak, a servant of the Church.

ALEXANDRA.

And since you are, so to speak, a true servant of the Church, why don't you convert Nicholas Ivanovich?

FATHER VASILY.

Everybody, if I may say so, has his own views on these subjects. And Nicholas Ivanovich, if I may say so, says much that is true. But on the main point he is in error concerning er—er—er— the Church.

ALEXANDRA.

And what are the true things that Nicholas Ivanovich says? Is it true that the Sermon on the Mount bids us give away our possessions to strangers, and let our family be beggars?

FATHER VASILY.

The family is, so to speak, held sacred in the Church, and the fathers of the Church have bestowed their blessing on the family, haven't they? But the highest perfection requires—well, yes, requires renunciation of earthly goods.

ALEXANDRA.

That is all very well for saints, but ordinary mortals ought simply to act like good Christians.

FATHER VASILY.

Nobody can tell what he was sent to earth for.

ALEXANDRA.

You are married, I suppose?

FATHER VASILY.

Certainly.

ALEXANDRA.

And have you got any children?

FATHER VASILY.

Yes, two.

ALEXANDRA.

Then why don't you renounce earthly joys, instead of smoking cigarettes?

FATHER VASILY.

It is, I may say, owing to my weakness and my unworthiness that I do not.

ALEXANDRA.

It seems to me that instead of bringing Nicholas Ivanovich to his senses, you are upholding him. I tell you frankly it is not right.

(Enter NURSE.*)*

Nurse.

Don't you hear baby crying? Please come to him.

Marie.

I'm coming—I'm coming.   (*Exit.*)

Alexandra.

I am so sorry for my sister. I see how she suffers. It is no easy matter to manage a household—seven children, and one of them a baby at the breast. And he with his new-fangled theories—I really think he is not quite right here (*points to her head*). Now tell me truly, what is this new religion you have discovered?

Father Vasily.

I don't quite understand, if I may say so.

Alexandra.

Please do not pretend you do not understand. You know perfectly well what I am asking.

Father Vasily.

But, pardon me——

Alexandra.

I ask you what this creed is, according to which you must shake hands with all peasants, allow them to cut down your forest, give them money for drink, and forsake your own family.

5

FATHER VASILY.

I do not know.

ALEXANDRA.

He says it is the Christian teaching. You are a priest of the Orthodox Church. Therefore you ought to know and ought to say whether the Christian teaching encourages stealing.

FATHER VASILY.

But I——

ALEXANDRA.

Otherwise, why do you call yourself a priest, and wear long hair and a cassock?

FATHER VASILY.

But we are never asked such things.

ALEXANDRA.

Really! Well, I ask you! Yesterday Nicholas Ivanovich said the Gospel command is, "Give to every man that asks." How is that to be interpreted?

FATHER VASILY.

I think in the simplest sense.

ALEXANDRA.

I do not think so at all. I think it means, as we were always taught, that everybody has what God has given him.

Father Vasily.

Of course, but still——

Alexandra.

It is quite evident that you are on his side. I was told you were ; and it is very wrong of you, I tell you quite frankly. If it were some schoolmistress, or some boy who accepted his every word —but you, in your position, ought to understand what your responsibilities are.

Father Vasily.

I try to.

Alexandra.

How can he be called religious when he does not go to church, and does not recognize the sacraments ? And you, instead of bringing him to reason, read Renan with him, and interpret the Gospel as you like.

Father Vasily

(*agitated*). I cannot answer. I am—I am—amazed, and would rather not say anything.

Alexandra.

Oh ! if I were a bishop I would teach you to read Renan and smoke cigarettes.

Peter.

Stop, for Heaven's sake ! By what right—— ?

Alexandra.

Please don't lecture me. I am sure Father Vasily does not mind. Well, I have said all I had to say. It would be much worse if I had any ill-feeling. Is not that so?

Father Vasily.

Pardon me if I have expressed myself badly— pardon me. (*Awkward silence.*)

(*Enter* Luba *and* Lisa.)

(Luba, *the daughter of* Marie Ivanovna, *is a pretty, energetic girl of twenty.* Lisa, *the daughter of* Alexandra Ivanovna, *is older. Both wear shawls on their heads, and carry baskets—they are going mushrooming in the woods. They greet* Alexandra Ivanovna, Peter Semenovich, *and the* Priest.)

Luba.

Where is mother?

Alexandra.

She has just gone to nurse the baby.

Peter.

Mind you bring back plenty of mushrooms. A village girl brought some beauties this morning. I would go with you, but it is so hot.

LISA.

Do come, father.

ALEXANDRA.

Yes, do go.   You are getting too **fat**.

PETER.

Very well.   But I must get some cigarettes.

(Exit.)

ALEXANDRA.

Where are all the other young people?

LUBA.

Stephen has gone to the station on his bicycle;
Mitrofan Dmitrich has gone to town with father;
the little ones are playing croquet; and Vania
is romping with the dogs in the porch.

ALEXANDRA.

Has Stephen come to any decision?

LUBA.

Yes, he is going to enlist as a volunteer.   He
was horribly rude to father yesterday.

ALEXANDRA.

Well, he has a good deal to bear.   Even a
worm will turn.   The boy wants to begin life,
and he is told to go and plough.

LUBA.

Father did not say that.   He said . . .

ALEXANDRA.

It makes no difference.   The boy must make a start, and whatever he proposes is found fault with.   Oh, there he is !

(*Enter* STEPHEN *on bicycle.*)

ALEXANDRA.

Talk of an angel and you hear his wings.   We were just speaking of you.   Luba says that you did not speak nicely to your father yesterday.

STEPHEN.

Not at all.   Nothing particular happened.   He expressed his opinion, and I expressed mine.   It is not my fault if our views do not agree.   Luba understands nothing, and is always ready to criticize.

ALEXANDRA.

What did you decide ?

STEPHEN.

I don't know what father decided.   I'm afraid he does not know himself ; but I have made up my mind to join the Horse Guards as a volunteer. It is only in our house that difficulties are raised

about everything. It is quite simple. I have
finished my studies ; I have got to do my military
service. It would be unpleasant to serve in the
army with coarse, drunken officers, so I shall join
the Guards, where I have friends.

ALEXANDRA.

Why did your father object ?

STEPHEN.

Father ? Oh, what's the good of talking about
him. He is infatuated with his *idée fixe*, and sees
only what he wants to see. He says that the
military is the most dastardly of all the services,
therefore I ought not to serve, and therefore he
gives me no money.

LISA.

No, Stephen, that was not what he said. I was
there. He said that if it is impossible to get out
of it, one should at least wait till one is called as a
recruit, but that to volunteer is to choose that
service oneself.

STEPHEN.

It is I, not he, who will serve. He was an
officer himself.

LISA.

He did not say that he would not give you

money, but that he could not participate in a matter that was contrary to all his principles.

STEPHEN.

Principles have nothing to do with it.   I've got to serve, and there's an end of it.

LISA.

I only said what I heard.

STEPHEN.

I know.   You agree with father in everything. Auntie, did you know that?   Lisa is always on father's side.

LISA.

When it is a question of justice.

ALEXANDRA.

Oh, I know Lisa is always on the side of nonsense.   She has a knack of finding it.   She scents it from afar.

> (*Enter* VANIA.   *He runs on to the veranda in a red blouse, accompanied by the dogs, with a telegram in his hand.*)

VANIA

(*to* LUBA).   Guess who is coming?

LUBA.

Why should I guess ?   Give me the telegram.
(*Stretches out her hand for it.*   VANIA *holds it out of
her reach.*)

VANIA.

I won't give it to you, and I won't tell you.   It
is some one who will make you blush.

LUBA.

Nonsense !   Who is it from ?

VANIA.

Aha ! You are blushing, you are !   Aunt Aline,
isn't it true that she's blushing ?

LUBA.

What nonsense !   Aunt Aline, who is it from ?

ALEXANDRA.

The Cheremshanovs.

LUBA.

Oh !

VANIA.

" Oh ! " indeed.   Why are you blushing ?

LUBA.

Auntie, show me the telegram.   (*Reads*) " Arrive by mail train ; all three.—Cheremshanovs."

5 *a*

That means the Princess, Boris, and Tonia. Well, I am very glad.

VANIA.

Of course you are very glad. Stephen, see how she's blushing.

STEPHEN.

Oh, drop it. You keep on saying the same thing over and over again.

VANIA.

You say that because you're a bit smitten by Tonia yourself. You'll have to draw lots, because sister and brother may not marry brother and sister.

STEPHEN.

Don't talk such rubbish. You'd better be careful. I've warned you several times.

LISA.

If they come by the mail train they ought to be here directly.

LUBA.

That's true. Then we had better not go out.

(*Enter* PETER SEMENOVICH *with cigarettes.*)

LUBA.

Uncle Peter, we are not going.

PETER.

Why?

LUBA.

The Cheremshanovs will be here directly. We had better have one set at tennis before they arrive. Stephen, will you play?

STEPHEN.

All right.

LUBA.

Vania and I against you and Lisa. Agreed? Well, then, I'll go and get the balls and call the village children. (*Exit.*)

PETER.

So much for my walk.

FATHER VASILY

(*rising to go*). Good-bye.

ALEXANDRA.

Oh, wait a little, Father Vasily. I want to talk to you, and Nicholas Ivanovich will soon be here.

FATHER VASILY

(*sits down and lights another cigarette*). He may be some time yet.

ALEXANDRA.

A carriage has just driven up ; I expect it is he.

PETER.

Which Princess Cheremshanova is it ? Is it possible that her maiden name was Golitsine ?

ALEXANDRA.

Yes, yes, that nice Princess Cheremshanova who lived in Rome with her aunt.

PETER.

I shall be glad to see her. I have not seen her since the time when we used to sing duets together in Rome. She sang very well. She has two children, I believe.

ALEXANDRA.

Yes, and they are both coming with her.

PETER.

I did not know they were so intimate with the Sarintsevs.

ALEXANDRA.

They are not intimate ; but they were abroad

together last year, and I believe that the Princess has designs on Luba for her son. She knows a thing or two.

PETER.

The Cheremshanovs were rich themselves.

ALEXANDRA.

They were. The Prince is still alive, but he has dissipated his fortune, and has taken to drink. She petitioned the Tsar, saved a few crumbs, and left him. But she brought up her children splendidly. The daughter is an excellent musician, and the son went through the university, and is very nice. Still I do not think Masha is particularly pleased. This is not a time for guests. Ah, there is Nicholas.

(*Enter* NICHOLAS IVANOVICH.)

NICHOLAS.

Good-morning, Aline. Hallo! Peter Semenovich. (*To the* PRIEST) How do you do, Vasily Ermilovich? (*He shakes hands.*)

ALEXANDRA.

There is some coffee here. Shall I pour it out? It is not very hot, but it can be warmed up. (*She rings.*)

NICHOLAS.

No, thank you ; I have had breakfast.   Where is Masha ?

ALEXANDRA.

She is nursing the baby.

NICHOLAS.

Is she well ?

ALEXANDRA.

Pretty well.   Have you done all your business ?

NICHOLAS.

Yes.   I think I will have some tea or some coffee if there is any.   (*To the* PRIEST) Have you brought the book ?   Have you read it ?   I have been thinking about you all the way.

(*Enter* FOOTMAN; *bows.* NICHOLAS *shakes hands with him.*)

ALEXANDRA

(*shrugging her shoulders, and exchanging glances with her husband*).   Heat up the samovar, please.

NICHOLAS.

Never mind, Aline.   I do not want anything ; and if I do, I can drink it as it is.

MISSIE

(*seeing her father, runs from the croquet ground, and clasps her arms round his neck*). Father, come along.

NICHOLAS

(*fondling her*). Directly, directly. Let me have something to drink. Go and play. I will come soon. (*Sits down at the table, drinks tea, and eats.*)

ALEXANDRA.

Were they found guilty?

NICHOLAS.

Yes. They pleaded guilty. (*To the* PRIEST) I imagine Renan did not convince you.

ALEXANDRA.

But you disagreed with the verdict?

NICHOLAS

(*annoyed*). Of course I did. (*To the* PRIEST) The main question for you lies, not in the divinity of Christ, not in the history of Christianity, but in the Church . . .

ALEXANDRA.

How was that? They confessed themselves: you gave them the lie. They were not stealing, only taking . . .

NICHOLAS

(*begins speaking to the* PRIEST, *then turning decidedly to* ALEXANDRA IVANOVNA). My dear Aline, do not worry me with innuendos and pin-pricks.

ALEXANDRA.

I am not doing anything of the sort.

NICHOLAS.

If you really want to know why I cannot prosecute the peasants for cutting down some trees which they badly needed . . .

ALEXANDRA.

I dare say they need this samovar also.

NICHOLAS.

Well, if you want me to tell you why I cannot allow men to be imprisoned for felling ten trees in a wood that is considered mine . . .

ALEXANDRA.

Considered so by every one.

PETER.

There you are, arguing again. I shall go out with the dogs. (*He leaves the veranda.*)

NICHOLAS.

Even supposing I were to consider that wood

mine—though that is impossible—we have 2,250 acres of forest, with approximately 200 trees on each—I think that makes about 450,000 in all. They felled 10—that is $\frac{1}{45000}$ part. Well, is it worth while, is it possible, to drag a man away from his family and put him in prison for such a thing?

Stephen.

Well, if you don't prosecute for this $\frac{1}{45000}$ part, the rest of the 450,000 will also soon be felled.

Nicholas.

I only gave that answer in reply to your aunt. In reality, I have no right to this forest. The land belongs to all—that is, to no individual—and we personally have never done a stroke of work on it.

Stephen.

Oh, no! You saved up, and you looked after the land.

Nicholas.

How did I get enough to save up, and when did I ever look after the forest myself? But there! you can't prove such things to a man who feels no shame in injuring others.

Stephen.

No one is injuring others.

NICHOLAS.

If he is not ashamed of being idle—of living on the labour of others—it cannot be proved, and all the political economy you learnt at the university only serves to justify your position.

STEPHEN.

On the contrary, science destroys all prejudices.

NICHOLAS.

Well, that does not matter. What does matter to me is the fact that if I were in Ephraim's place I should do just what he did ; and having done it I should be in despair if I were imprisoned, and therefore, since I *would do unto others as I would be done by*, I cannot prosecute him, and must do my best to get him off.

PETER.

But, in that case, it is not possible to own anything.

ALEXANDRA.

Then it is much more profitable to steal than to work.

STEPHEN.

You never answer one's arguments. I say that he who economizes has a right to use his savings.

Together.

NICHOLAS

(*smiling*).   I do not know which of you to answer.
(*To* PETER) It is not possible to own anything.

ALEXANDRA.

If that is so, one cannot have clothes or a crust
of bread.   One must give up everything, and life
becomes impossible.

NICHOLAS.

It is impossible to live as we live.

STEPHEN.

Then we must die.   Therefore that teaching is
no good for life.

NICHOLAS.

On the contrary, it is given only for life.   Yes,
we must relinquish everything—not only a forest
by which we profit, though we have never seen it,
but we should give up our clothes and our bread
even.

ALEXANDRA.

And the children's bread also ?

NICHOLAS.

Yes, the children's also—and not bread only—
we must give up ourselves.   That is the whole
teaching of Christ.   We must use all our efforts
to give up ourselves.

STEPHEN.

To die, therefore ?

NICHOLAS.

Yes, if you die *for others* it would be good both for yourself and for others ; but the fact remains that man is not simply a spirit, but a spirit in the flesh ; and the flesh impels us to live for self, while the enlightened spirit urges us to live for God, for others ; and the result of this conflict makes us take a middle course.   The nearer we attain to God the better.   Therefore the more we try to live for God the better.   The flesh will make sufficient efforts on its own account.

STEPHEN.

Why take a middle course ?   If such a life is best, then one should give up everything and die.

NICHOLAS.

It would be splendid.   Try to do it, and you will find it good for you as well as for others.

ALEXANDRA.

No, all this is neither clear nor simple.   It is dragged in by the hair.

NICHOLAS.

What am I to do ?   I cannot make you understand.   Enough of this !

STEPHEN.

Enough, indeed! I do not understand. (*Exit.*)

NICHOLAS

(*to the* PRIEST). Well, what did you think of the book?

FATHER VASILY

(*agitated*). I hardly know what to say. The historical side is sufficiently studied, but it is hardly convincingly or satisfactorily proved — perhaps because the data are insufficient. You cannot prove the divinity or non-divinity of Christ historically. There is only one unanswerable proof . . .

> (*During the conversation all, one after the other, leave the room—first the* LADIES, *then* STEPHEN, *and finally* PETER SEMENOVICH, *leaving the* PRIEST *and* NICHOLAS *alone.*)

NICHOLAS.

You mean the Church?

FATHER VASILY.

Yes, of course, the Church; the testimony of men—well, of truly holy men, shall we say?

NICHOLAS.

It would certainly be excellent if such an infallible authority existed which we could trust, and it is desirable that it should exist. But its desirability is no proof that it does exist.

FATHER VASILY.

I contend that it does prove it. God could not, as it were, let His law be distorted, be badly interpreted ; and He had to institute a—well—a custodian of His truths. He had to, hadn't He, to prevent the distortion of these truths ?

NICHOLAS.

Very well ; but you set out to prove the truths themselves, and now you are proving the truth of the custodians.

FATHER VASILY.

Well, in regard to that, we must, so to speak, believe.

NICHOLAS.

Believe ? We cannot live without belief. We must believe, but not what others tell us ; only what we are led to by the course of our own thoughts, our own reason . . . the belief in God, in the true life everlasting.

FATHER VASILY.

Reason may deceive you—each man has his own——

NICHOLAS

(*warmly*). That is horrible blasphemy ! God has
given us one holy instrument by which to know
the truth—one that can unite us all, and we
distrust it !

FATHER VASILY.

But how can we trust it when there is so much
difference of opinion—isn't there ?

NICHOLAS.

Where is there any difference of opinion as to
two and two making four ; as to our not doing to
others what we do not wish to be done to ourselves ; as to there being a cause for everything ;
and such truths as these ?   We all recognize these
truths because they are in accordance with our
reason.   As to such questions as what God revealed
to Moses on Mount Sinai, whether or not Buddha
flew away on a sunbeam, or whether Mohammed
and Christ flew up to heaven—and things of that
sort—we all disagree.

FATHER VASILY.

No, we do not all disagree.   All who have the
truth are united in one faith in the God Christ.

NICHOLAS.

You are not united then because you all differ,

so why should I believe you rather than a Buddhist lama ?   Simply because I happened to be born in your faith ?

> (*Sounds of dispute from the tennis-court.* "*Out.*" "*No, it was not.*" "*I saw it.*"
>
> *During the conversation the* FOOT-MAN *rearranges the table, bringing in fresh tea and coffee.*)

NICHOLAS

(*continuing*).   You say the Church gives union.   But, on the contrary, the worst differences were always caused by the Church.   "How often would I have gathered Thy children together, even as a hen gathereth her chickens under her wings."

FATHER VASILY.

It was so before Christ.   Christ united all.

NICHOLAS.

Christ united us all, but we became disunited because we understood Him wrongly.   He destroyed all Churches.

FATHER VASILY.

Then what does "tell the Church" mean ?

NICHOLAS.

It is not a question of words, nor do these words apply to the Church. The whole thing is the spirit of the teaching. Christ's teaching is universal, and contains all beliefs, and does not contain anything that is exclusive—neither the resurrection, nor the divinity of Christ, nor the sacraments—indeed, nothing that can disunite.

FATHER VASILY.

Well, that is your interpretation of the Christian teaching; but the Christian teaching is entirely founded on the divinity of Christ and His resurrection.

NICHOLAS.

That is why Churches are so horrible. They disunite by declaring that they possess the full, certain, and infallible truth—"filling us with the Holy Ghost." It began with the first meeting of the apostles. From that moment they began to affirm that they were possessed of full and *exclusive* truth. Why, if I say that there is a God, that the world began, all will agree with me, and this recognition of God will unite us; but if I say there is a god Brahma, or a Jewish god, or a Trinity— such a divinity disunites. Men want to unite and invent a means to that end, but they disregard the only certain means of union—an aspiration after truth.   It is as if in a great building, where the light falls from the roof on to the middle of the floor, men were to stand in groups in the corners instead of going into the light.   If they went into the light they would, without thinking about it, be united.

FATHER VASILY.

But how would you guide the people without having, so to speak, a fixed truth ?

NICHOLAS.

That is the horror of it.   Each of us has his own soul to save, has God's work to do, and we are all anxious about saving and teaching others.   And what do we teach them ?   It is simply horrible to think that at the end of the nineteenth century we are teaching that God created the world in six days, then sent a flood, putting all the animals into the Ark, and all the absurd nonsense of the Old Testament ; and then that Christ ordered us to be baptized in water, or the absurdity of the redemption without which you cannot be saved ; then that Christ flew away to skies which do not exist, and there sits at the right hand of God the Father. We are accustomed to all this, but really it is terrible.   A pure child, open to good and truth, asks us what the world is, what its law is, and instead of teaching him the love and truth which we have believed, we carefully stuff his head with all sorts of dreadful, absurd lies and horrors, ascribing them all to God. This is awful. It is a crime that nothing can surpass. And we, and you with your Church, do all this. Forgive me.

FATHER VASILY.

Yes, if you look at Christ's teaching in that way —rationally, so to speak—then it is so.

NICHOLAS.

It is the same, no matter in what way you look at it.

(*Silence. The* PRIEST *takes leave of him. Enter* ALEXANDRA IVAN-OVNA.)

ALEXANDRA.

Good-bye, Father Vasily. Do not listen to him ; he will lead you astray.

FATHER VASILY.

Oh no ! One must put the Gospel to the test. It is too important a matter to be neglected, isn't it ?
(*Exit.*)

ALEXANDRA.

Really, Nicholas, you have no pity on him. Though he is a priest, he is little more than a boy.

He cannot have settled convictions; he cannot be steadfast. . . .

NICHOLAS.

Are we to let him become confirmed in them, to harden in deceit? Why should we? Ah, he is a good, sincere man.

ALEXANDRA.

Well, what would happen to him were he to believe you?

NICHOLAS.

It is not a question of believing me; but if he could see the truth it would be well for him and for every one.

ALEXANDRA.

If it were really well, all would believe you. As it is, we see just the contrary. No one believes you—your wife least of all. She cannot believe you.

NICHOLAS.

Who told you so?

ALEXANDRA.

Well, explain all this to Masha. She never understood and never will, and no one in the world ever will, understand why you should take care of strangers and neglect your own children. Explain that to Masha.

NICHOLAS.

Masha is sure to understand. Forgive me, Aline, but if it were not for outside influences, to which she is so susceptible, she would understand me and go hand-in-hand with me.

ALEXANDRA.

To deprive her own children for the drunken Ephraim and Co.? Never. As for your being angry with me, you will excuse me, but I cannot help speaking . . .

NICHOLAS.

I am not angry. On the contrary, I am very glad that you said all you had to say, and gave me the opportunity of giving all my own views. I thought it over on my way to-day, and I am going to tell her at once, and you will see that she will agree, for she is both wise and good.

ALEXANDRA.

You will allow me to have my doubts.

NICHOLAS.

Well, I have none. This is no invention of mine : it is what we all know, and what Christ revealed to us.

ALEXANDRA.

You think He revealed *this?* I think He revealed something quite different.

NICHOLAS.

There can be nothing different. Just listen. Do not argue ; listen to me.

ALEXANDRA.

I am listening.

NICHOLAS.

You admit that at any minute we may die and return to nothingness or to God, who demands that we should live according to His will.

ALEXANDRA.

Well ?

NICHOLAS.

Well, what else am I to do in this life but that which the highest Judge that is in my soul—my conscience, God—demands ? My conscience, God, demands that I should consider all men equal, should love and serve all.

ALEXANDRA.

Your children among the rest.

NICHOLAS.

Of course ; but I must do everything my conscience dictates. The most important thing of all is to recognize that my life does not belong to me, nor yours to you, but to God, who sent us and requires us to live according to His will. And His will . . .

ALEXANDRA.

And you will convince Masha of this ?

NICHOLAS.

Certainly.

ALEXANDRA.

She will cease to educate her children as she should and will desert them ?   Never.

NICHOLAS.

Not only she ; you too will understand that that is the only thing to do.

ALEXANDRA.

Never !

(*Enter* MARIE IVANOVNA.)

NICHOLAS.

Well, Masha, I hope I did not wake you up this morning.

MARIE.

No, I was not asleep.   Did you have a pleasant journey ?

NICHOLAS.

Yes, very pleasant.

MARIE.

Why are you drinking that cold tea ?   Anyhow, we must have some fresh made for our guests. You know that Princess Cheremshanova is coming with her son and daughter.

NICHOLAS.

If you are pleased, so am I.

MARIE.

Yes. I am very fond of her and of her children, but it is hardly the moment for visitors.

ALEXANDRA.

Well, have a talk with him, and I will go and watch the game.

>(*A silence, after which* MARIE
>IVANOVNA *and* NICHOLAS IVANOVICH
>*both speak at once.*)

MARIE.

Together. {

It is hardly the moment, because we must talk things over.

NICHOLAS.

I was just telling Aline . . .

MARIE.

What?

NICHOLAS.

No; you speak.

MARIE.

Well, I wanted to talk to you about Stephen. Something must be decided. The poor boy is in suspense, does not know what is going to happen, and comes to me ; but how can I decide ?

NICHOLAS.

How can any one decide? He can decide for himself.

MARIE.

Why, you know he wants to enter the Guards as a volunteer, and he cannot do it without a certificate from you, and he must have money, and you give him nothing (*agitated*).

NICHOLAS.

Masha, for Heaven's sake do not get agitated, and listen to me. I neither give nor refuse. To enter the military service voluntarily I consider foolish madness, such as only a savage is capable of. If he does not understand the meanness, the baseness of such an action, or if he does it out of self-interest——

MARIE.

Oh, everything seems mad and foolish to you now. He wants to live—*you* have lived.

NICHOLAS

(*hotly*). I lived without understanding, with no one to tell me. But it depends on him now —not on me.

MARIE.

But it does depend on you, when you give him no money.

NICHOLAS.

I cannot give what does not belong to me.

MARIE.

What do you mean by " does not belong to me " ?

NICHOLAS.

The labour of others does not belong to me. To give him money, I must take from others. I have no right to ; I cannot. So long as I am the master of the estate I cannot dispose of it otherwise than as my conscience dictates. I cannot spend the labour of peasants, which costs them their whole strength, on the drinking-bouts of a hussar. Take the estate from me ; then I shall not be responsible.

MARIE.

You know I do not want that, and I cannot do it. I have to educate the children, to nurse them, to bring them into the world. It is cruel.

NICHOLAS.

Dearest Masha, that is not the point. When you began to speak, I began also, and I wanted so

to talk frankly to you. All this is impossible.
We live together, and do not understand each
other; sometimes it seems as though we misunder-
stood each other on purpose.

MARIE.

I want to understand you, but I cannot. I
cannot understand what has come over you.

NICHOLAS.

Then try to understand now. It is hardly the
moment, but Heaven knows when there will be
a moment. Try to understand not only me, but
yourself and your own life. We cannot go on
living without knowing what we live for.

MARIE.

We lived so before, and we lived very well.
(*Noting an expression of displeasure on his face*) All
right; I am listening.

NICHOLAS.

I used to live thus, thus—that is to say, without
thinking why I lived; but the time came when
I was aghast. We live on the labour of others,
we make others work for us, we bring children
into the world, and educate them for the same
thing. Old age, death, will come, and I shall

ask myself, "What did I live for? To produce parasites like myself?" Besides, this life is not even amusing. It is only tolerable when one is overflowing with the energy of life, like Vania.

MARIE.

Every one lives like that.

NICHOLAS.

And every one is unhappy.

MARIE.

Not at all.

NICHOLAS.

I, at least, discovered that I was terribly unhappy, and that I was causing you and the children to be unhappy, and I asked myself, "Is it possible that God created you for this?" And directly I thought that, I felt that the answer was "No." Then I asked myself, "What *did* God create us for?"

(*A* FOOTMAN *enters.* MARIE IVANOVNA *does not listen to her husband, but speaks to the* FOOTMAN.)

MARIE.

Bring some hot milk.

NICHOLAS.

I found the answer in the Gospel : we do not live for ourselves at all. It was revealed to me clearly once when I was thinking over the parable of the labourers in the vineyard. Do you remember it ?

MARIE.

Yes ; I know the labourers.

NICHOLAS.

Somehow or other that parable showed me my mistake more clearly than anything. I had believed that my life was my own just as those labourers believed that the vineyard was theirs, and everything was terrible to me. But as soon as I realized that my life was not my own, that I was sent into the world to do the work of God——

MARIE.

What of that ? We all know that.

NICHOLAS.

Well, if we know it, we cannot continue to live as we do, when we know our whole life is not a fulfilment of this will, but, on the contrary, is in perpetual contradiction to it.

MARIE.

In what way is it a contradiction when we do no harm to any one?

NICHOLAS.

How can you say we do no harm to any one? That is exactly the conception of life that the labourers in the vineyard had. We——

MARIE.

Oh yes; I know the parable. Well, what of it? He gave them all the same portion.

NICHOLAS

(*after a silence*). No; that is not it. But think of this, Masha; we have only one life, and it is in our power to live it devoutly or to ruin it.

MARIE.

I cannot think and discuss. I get no sleep at night; I am nursing baby. I manage the whole household, and instead of helping me you keep on telling me things I do not understand.

NICHOLAS.

Masha!

MARIE.

And now these visitors are arriving.

NICHOLAS.

But we will talk it out to the end, shall we not?
(*He kisses her.*)   Yes?

MARIE.

Yes.   But do be your former self.

NICHOLAS.

That I cannot.   But listen to me——
> (*The sound of approaching carriage
> bells and wheels is heard.*)

MARIE.

There is no time now—they have arrived.   I
must go to them.

> (*Disappears round the corner of the
> house, followed by* STEPHEN *and* LUBA.
> ALEXANDRA IVANOVNA *and her hus-
> band and* LISA *come on to the veranda.*
> NICHOLAS IVANOVICH *walks about in
> deep thought.*)

VANIA

(*jumping over a bench*).   I don't give in; we'll
finish the game!   Well, Luba?

LUBA

(*seriously*).   No nonsense, please!

Alexandra.

Well, have you convinced her?

Nicholas.

Aline, what is going on between us now is serious, and jokes are quite out of place. It is not I who am convincing her, but life, truth, God. Therefore she cannot help being convinced—if not to-day, then to-morrow ; if not to-morrow— The worst of it all is that no one ever has time. Who has come?

Peter.

The Cheremshanovs — Katia Cheremshanova, whom I have not seen for eighteen years. The last time we met we sang together, "La ei darem la mano." (*He sings.*)

Alexandra

(*to her husband*). Please do not interfere, and do not imagine that I have quarrelled with Nicholas. I am speaking the truth. (*To* Nicholas) I was not joking in the least, but it seemed so strange that you wanted to convince Masha at the very moment when she wanted to talk matters over with you.

Nicholas.

Very well, very well. Here they are. Please tell Masha that I am in my room. (*Exit.*)

ACT II.

SCENE I.

Same place in the country. Time: One week later. Scene represents large drawing-room. Table is laid with samovar, tea, and coffee. Piano against the wall; music-rack. MARIE IVANOVNA, *the* PRINCESS, *and* PETER SEMENOVICH *are seated at the table.*

PETER.

Yes, Princess. It does not seem so long ago that you used to sing "Rosine," and I . . . Whereas now I should not even do for a Don Basilio.

PRINCESS.

Now the children might sing, but times have altered.

PETER.

Yes, they are positivists. But I hear your daughter is a very serious and excellent musician. Are they still asleep?

6 a

Marie.

Yes, they went out riding by moonlight and returned very late.   I was nursing baby and heard them.

Peter.

And when does my better half return ?   Have you sent the carriage for her ?

Marie.

Yes, it went a long time ago.   She ought to be here soon.

Princess.

Did Alexandra Ivanovna really go with the sole purpose of fetching Father Gerasim ?

Marie.

Yes, the thought suddenly struck her yesterday, and she flew off at once.

Princess.

What energy !   I admire it.

Peter.

Oh, as to that, it never fails us.   (*Takes out a cigar.*)   Well, I think I'll take a turn in the park with the dogs and smoke while the young people are getting up.

PRINCESS.

I don't know, dear Marie Ivanovna, but I really think you take it too much to heart. I understand him. He is full of such high aspiration. What does it matter if he does give his property away to the poor? It's only too true that we all think too much of ourselves.

MARIE.

Oh, if it were only that. But you don't know him—you do not know all. It is not only helping the poor. It is a complete change—the utter wrecking of everything.

PRINCESS.

I certainly do not wish to intrude into your family life, but if you would allow me . . .

MARIE.

But I look on you as one of the family, especially now.

PRINCESS.

I should just advise you to put your demands plainly before him, and openly come to some agreement with him as to the limits——

MARIE

(*agitated*). There are no limits! He wishes to

give everything away. He wants me at my age to become a cook—a laundress.

PRINCESS.

Oh, impossible ! How extraordinary !

MARIE

(*taking out a letter*). Now we are quite alone, I should like to tell you everything. Yesterday he wrote me this letter. I will read it to you.

PRINCESS.

What ! living in the same house with you, he writes you letters ? How strange !

MARIE.

Oh no. I quite understand. He gets so excited when he talks I have been feeling anxious about his health lately.

PRINCESS.

Well, what does he write ?

MARIE.

Listen. (*She reads*) "You reproach me for destroying our former life without offering you anything else or saying how I intend to provide for my family. When we begin to talk we both get excited, so I am writing instead. I have told you many times why I can't go on living as I have done.   And as for trying to convince you that it is wrong to live as we have been accustomed to do, that we must lead a Christian life, I cannot do that in a letter.   You can do one of two things —either believe in truth and liberty and go with me, or believe in me, give yourself trustfully to me, and follow me."   (*Stops reading.*) But I can do neither of these things!   I do not believe that I ought to live as he desires, and moreover I love the children and I cannot trust him.   (*Continues to read*) "My plan is this. We will give all our land to the peasants, leaving ourselves fifty acres and the kitchen garden and the flooded meadow.   We will try to work, but we will not force ourselves or our children to work. What we reserve for ourselves will bring in about five hundred roubles * a year."

PRINCESS.

It is impossible to live on five hundred roubles a year with seven children.

MARIE.

Well, and then he goes on to say that we will give up our house for a school and live in the gardener's cottage, in two rooms.

* A rouble = about 2s.

PRINCESS.

Yes, I really begin to think that he's not well. What have you answered ?

MARIE.

I told him I could not agree to it. That, were I alone, I would follow him anywhere. But with the children . . . Just think—I am nursing little Nicholas. I told him it was impossible to break up everything like that. Was this what I married him for ? I am already old and feeble. It is not an easy matter to bring nine children into the world and nurse them.

PRINCESS.

I never dreamt it had gone so far !

MARIE.

Well, that is how matters stand, and I can't imagine what will become of us. Yesterday he remitted the entire rent of the peasants from Dmitrovka, and he intends to give that land to them outright.

PRINCESS.

I really think you ought not to permit that. It is our duty to protect our children. If he cannot own his estate himself, let him give it to you.

MARIE.

I don't want it.

PRINCESS.

But it is your duty to retain it, for the sake of your children. Let him make it over to you.

MARIE.

My sister suggested that to him, but he said he had no right to dispose of it, as the land belonged to those who tilled it, and it was his duty to give it to the peasants.

PRINCESS.

Yes, I see it is really much more serious than I thought.

MARIE.

And fancy ! our priest is on his side.

PRINCESS.

I noticed that yesterday.

MARIE.

Now my sister has gone to Moscow to consult a lawyer, and above all to bring Father Gerasim back with her to see if he has any influence with him.

PRINCESS.

I do not think that Christianity consists in ruining one's own family.

MARIE.

But he will not trust Father Gerasim. He is too far confirmed in his convictions, and you know when he talks I can find no arguments to use against him. The worst of it is—I believe he is right.

PRINCESS.

That is only because you love him.

MARIE.

I do not know why, but it is dreadful, dreadful. Everything remains unsettled. That's what religion does !

(*Enter* NURSE.)

NURSE.

Please, ma'am, the baby is awake and wants you.

MARIE.

I will come in a moment. I am worried, and the baby has colic, you see. I am coming.

(*Exit* PRINCESS.)

(*From the other side enters* NICHOLAS *with a paper in his hand.*)

NICHOLAS.

It is incredible !

MARIE.

What is the matter ?

NICHOLAS.

The matter is just this, that for a pine tree of ours Peter is to go to jail.

MARIE.

But why?

NICHOLAS.

Because he felled it. They took the matter to court, and he is sentenced to a month's imprisonment. His wife came to implore me——

MARIE.

Well, can't you help her?

NICHOLAS.

I cannot now. The only thing to do is not to own any forest, and I will not! I will just go and see if I can help in the trouble of which I myself have been the cause.

(*Enter* LUBA *and* BORIS.)

LUBA.

Good-morning, father. (*Kisses him.*) Where are you going?

NICHOLAS.

I have just come from the village and I'm now on my way back. A hungry man is being put in jail for——

LUBA.

It's probably Peter.

NICHOLAS.

Yes—Peter.

(*Exeunt* NICHOLAS *and* MARIE IVANOVNA.)

LUBA.

(*sitting down before the samovar*).   Will you take coffee or tea?

BORIS.

I do not care.

LUBA.

Things are just as they were.   I cannot see how it will end.

BORIS.

I do not quite understand him.   I know the peasants are poor and ignorant, that it's our duty to help them.   But not by showing favour to thieves.

LUBA.

But how ?

BORIS.

By everything we do.   We must dedicate all our knowledge to them, but we cannot give up our life.

LUBA.

Father says that is just what we must do.

BORIS.

I do not see why. It is quite possible to help the people without ruining one's own life, and that is what I intend doing myself. If only you——

LUBA.

Your wishes are mine. And I am not afraid of anything.

BORIS.

But what about your ear-rings, and your dress?

LUBA.

The ear-rings we can sell, and as for the frock, I might dress differently without being altogether ugly.

BORIS.

I want to have another talk with him. Do you think I should be in his way if I went to the village?

LUBA.

I'm sure you wouldn't. I can see he is very fond of you. Yesterday he talked to you nearly all the time.

BORIS.

Then I'll go.

LUBA.

Yes, do. And I'll go and wake up Lisa and Tonia.

(Exit on different sides.)

SCENE II.

Village street.   The peasant IVAN ZIABREV *is lying on the ground at a cottage door with a sheepskin coat over him.*

IVAN.

Malashka !   (*From behind the cottage comes a little girl with a baby in her arms.   The baby cries.*)   I want a drink of water.   (MALASHKA *goes into the cottage.   The baby is heard crying still.   She brings a jug of water.*)   Why do you hit the baby and make him howl ?   I'll tell your mother.

MALASHKA.

Do tell mother !   Baby's howling because he's hungry.

IVAN

(*drinking*).   Why don't you go and get some milk at Demkin's ?

MALASHKA.

I have been.   They haven't got any, and there was not a soul at home.

IVAN.

Oh, I wish Death would come quicker.   Has the dinner bell rung ?

MALASHKA

(*screaming at the top of her voice*). Yes, it has rung ! There's the master coming !

(*Enter* NICHOLAS.)

NICHOLAS.

Why are you lying out here ?

IVAN.

There are flies there.   And it's too hot.

NICHOLAS.

Have you got warm then ?

IVAN.

I feel as if I were on fire now.

NICHOLAS.

Where is Peter ?   At home ?

IVAN.

How could he be, at this hour ?   He's gone to the fields to bring in the sheaves.

NICHOLAS.

I was told he had been arrested.

IVAN.

That's quite true.   The policeman has gone to the field after him.

> (*Enter a pregnant* WOMAN, *with a sheaf of oats and a pitchfork, and immediately hits* MALASHKA *over the head*.)

WOMAN.

Why did you go away from the baby?   Do listen to him screaming.   You only think of running out in the road.

MALASHKA

(*crying loudly*).   I just came out to give father a drink of water.

WOMAN.

I'll give it you.   (*Sees* NICHOLAS IVANOVICH.) Good-day, Nicholas Ivanovich.   You see what they are all bringing me to!   There's no one but me to do anything, and I'm worn out.   Now they're taking our very last man to jail, and this lazy lout is lying about doing nothing.

NICHOLAS.

Why do you say that?   You can see he is ill.

WOMAN.

Ill, indeed!   What about me?   When there's

work to be done then he's sick, but if he wants to go on the spree and knock me about, he's well enough. Let him die like a dog. I don't care.

NICHOLAS.

How sinful to talk like that!

WOMAN.

I know it's a sin. But my temper gets the better of me. Look how I am, and I have to work for two. All the others have got their oats in, and a quarter of our field isn't cut yet. I ought not to have stopped, but I had to come home and see after the children.

NICHOLAS.

I will have your oats cut for you and will send some binders out to your field.

WOMAN.

Oh, I can manage the binding myself, if we can only get it cut. Oh, Nicholas Ivanovich, do you think he's going to die? He's very low indeed.

NICHOLAS.

I'm sure I don't know; but he's certainly very weak. I think he had better be taken to the hospital.

WOMAN.

O my God! (*Begins to weep loudly.*) Don't

take him away.   Let him die here.   (*To the husband*) What did you say ?

IVAN.

I want to go to hospital.   I'm lying here worse than a dog.

WOMAN.

Oh, I don't know what to do !   I shall go mad ! Malashka, get dinner !

NICHOLAS.

And what have you got for dinner ?

WOMAN.

Some potatoes and bread.   That's all we've got. (*Goes into cottage, the sounds of a pig squealing and children crying are heard.*)

IVAN

(*groaning*).   O God, if Death would come !

(*Enter* BORIS.)

BORIS.

Can't I be of any use here ?

NICHOLAS.

No one can be of any use here.   The evil is too deeply rooted.   We can only be of use to ourselves by realizing on what foundations we build our happiness.   Here is a family—five children—the wife pregnant, the husband ill, and nothing in the house to eat but potatoes. And at this moment it is a question whether they will have food for next year. And there is no help for them. How can one help? I am going to hire a man to work for them. But who will that man be? A man as badly off as they are, who has given up tilling his own land through drunkenness or poverty.

Boris.

Excuse me, but if that is the case, why are you here?

Nicholas.

I am trying to ascertain my own position; to know who looks after our gardens, builds our houses, makes our clothes, feeds and dresses us.

> (Peasants *with scythes and* Women *with pitchforks pass them. They bow to the master.*)

Nicholas

(*stopping one of them*). Ephraim, can you take the job of cutting Ivan's oats for him?

Ephraim

(*shaking his head*). I'd do it gladly, but I can't. I haven't got my own in yet. I'm just hurrying off to do it now. Why? Is Ivan dying?

ANOTHER PEASANT.

There's old Sebastian.   Maybe he can take the job.   Sebastian! they want a man to reap.

SEBASTIAN.

Take the job yourself if you want it.   One day may mean the whole year in such weather as this.

NICHOLAS

(*to* BORIS).   All those men are half-starved, many of them ill or old, living on bread and water.   Look at that old man.   He suffers from rupture—and he works from four in the morning till ten at night, and is barely alive.   And we— now, is it possible, when we once understand this, to go on living quietly and calling ourselves Christians?   Can we call ourselves anything short of beasts?

BORIS.

But what are we to do?

NICHOLAS.

Not be a party to evil.   Not possess land. Not feed upon their toil.   How this can be managed I do not know.   The thing is—at least so it was with me.   I lived and did not understand what sort of life I led.   I didn't understand that I was a son of God and that we were all sons of

God and all brothers.   But when I came to understand that, when I saw that all had equal claims
on life, my whole life was changed.   I cannot explain it very well to you, I can only say that before,
I was blind, just as my family still are, but now
my eyes are opened I cannot help seeing.   And,
seeing, I cannot go on living as before.   But, of
course, for the present we must do as best we can.

(*Enter* Police Sergeant, *with*
Peter *and his wife and a boy.*)

Peter

(*falling on his knees before* Nicholas Ivanovich).
Forgive me, for Christ's sake.   I'm done for !
My wife can't get along alone.   Can't you let me
go on bail ?

Nicholas.

I will see about it.   I will write.   (*To the*
Police Sergeant) Couldn't you let him stay here
meanwhile ?

Sergeant.

I have orders to take him to the police-station.

Nicholas.

Go then ; I will hire a labourer.   I will do all
that is possible.   This is my fault.   How can one
live like this ?   (*Exit.*)

Scene III.

Same as first scene. It is raining outside. Drawing-room with a piano. Tonia *has just finished playing the Schumann Sonata, and is still sitting at the piano.* Stephen *stands near the piano. After the music,* Luba, Lisa, Anna Ivanovna, Mitrofan Dmitrich, *and the* Priest *are all greatly moved.*

Luba.

The Andante is so lovely.

Stephen.

No—the Scherzo !   But the whole thing is charming.

Lisa.

Beautiful !

Stephen

(*to* Tonia).   I had no idea you were such an artist.   Your rendering is masterly.   Difficulties do not seem to exist for you, you only think of the expression, and it is so exquisitely delicate.

Luba.

So noble, too !

TONIA.

I feel it is not what I want it to be. There's a great deal lacking in my playing.

LISA.

It could not be better. It is marvellous.

LUBA.

Schumann is very great. But I think Chopin appeals to the heart more.

STEPHEN.

He is more lyrical.

TONIA.

I do not think a comparison is possible.

LUBA.

Do you remember that Prelude of his?

TONIA.

Do you mean the so-called George Sand one?
(*Begins to play.*)

LUBA.

No, not that one. That is lovely, but it is hackneyed. Please play this one.

(TONIA *tries to play, but breaks off and stops.*)

LUBA.

No, the one in D minor.

TONIA.

Oh, this one. It is wonderful. It is like chaos before the Creation.

STEPHEN

(*laughs*). Yes, yes ; do play it. No, better not —you are tired. We have already had a wonderful morning, thanks to you.

> (TONIA *rises and looks out of the window.*)

TONIA.

There are the peasants again.

LUBA.

That's what is so precious in music. I understand Saul. I'm not tormented by the devil, but I know how Saul felt. There's no art that can make one forget everything like music.

TONIA.

And yet you are going to marry a man who doesn't understand music.

LUBA.

Oh, but—Boris does understand it.

BORIS

(*absent-minded*). Music ! Yes, I like music. But it isn't important. And I am rather sorry for the life that people lead who attach so much importance to it.

> (*There are sweets on the table and they all eat.*)

LUBA.

How nice to be engaged! Then one always has sweets.

BORIS.

Oh, it is not I—it's mother.

TONIA.

Very nice of her. (*Goes to the window.*) Whom do you want to see? The peasants have come to see Nicholas Ivanovich.

LUBA

(*going to the window*). He is not at home. Wait.

TONIA.

And what about poetry?

LUBA.

No, the value of music is that it takes hold of you, and carries you away from reality. We were all so gloomy just now, and when you began to play, everything brightened. It did really. Take the waltzes of Chopin. They're hackneyed, of course, but——

TONIA.

This one? (*She plays.*)

SCENE IV.

(*Enter* NICHOLAS. *He greets* TONIA, LUBA, STEPHEN, *and* LISA.)

NICHOLAS

(*to* LUBA).   Where's mother?

LUBA.

I think she is in the nursery.   Father, how wonderfully Tonia plays.   Where have you been?

NICHOLAS.

In the village.

(STEPHEN *calls the* FOOTMAN, *who enters.*)

STEPHEN.

Bring another samovar.

NICHOLAS

(*shakes hands with* FOOTMAN).   Good-morning!

(FOOTMAN *confused.   Exit.   Exit also* NICHOLAS.)

STEPHEN.

Poor chap!   He's so embarrassed.   He doesn't understand.   It's as if we were all guilty somehow.

NICHOLAS

(*re-enters*).   I was going to my room without telling you what I felt.   I think it was wrong of
me. (*To* TONIA) If you, who are our guest,
are hurt by what I am going to say, please forgive
me, as I must speak.   You said just now, Luba,
that Tonia played well.   Here you are, seven or
eight healthy young men and women.   You slept
till ten o'clock.   Then you had food and drink,
and you are still eating, and you play and discuss
music.   And there, where I have just come from,
the people are up at three in the morning.   Some
have not slept at all, having watched the cattle all
night ; and all of them, even the old, the sick, and
the children, and the women with babies at the
breast and those who are about to have children,
work with their utmost strength, that we may
enjoy the fruits of their labour.   And as if that
were not enough, one of them, the only worker
in the family, is just now being dragged to prison
because in the spring he cut down a pine tree
in the forest which is called mine—one of the
hundred thousand that grow there.   Here we
are, washed and dressed, having left all our
uncleanness in the bedrooms for slaves to carry
away.   Eating, drinking, or discussing which
touches us more, Schumann or Chopin, and

7

which of them drives away our *ennui* the more effectually. That is what I thought on seeing you all just now, and so tell you. Just think whether it is possible to go on like that! (*Standing in great agitation.*)

LISA.

It is true—quite true.

LUBA.

Thinking as you do, life is impossible.

STEPHEN.

Why is it impossible? I don't see why we shouldn't talk about Schumann even though the peasants are poor. The one doesn't exclude the other. If men——

NICHOLAS

(*angrily*). If a man has no heart and is made of wood——

STEPHEN.

Well, I will be silent.

TONIA.

This problem is terrible. And it is the problem of our time. We must not be afraid of it. We must look reality in the face in order to solve it.

Nicholas.

There is no time to wait for the problem to be solved by concerted action. Each of us may die to-day or to-morrow. How am I to live without suffering from this inner conflict?

Boris.

Of course the only way is not to share in the evil.

Nicholas.

Well, forgive me if I have hurt you. I could not help saying what I felt. (*Exit.*)

Stephen.

How could we avoid sharing in it? Our whole life is bound up with it.

Boris.

That is exactly why he says that in the first place one ought not to possess property, and one's whole life should be so altered that one may serve others, and not be served by them.

Tonia.

Oh, I see you are quite on Nicholas Ivanovich's side.

Boris.

Yes, I begin to understand for the first time; and, besides, all I saw in the village. We have only to take off the spectacles through which we are accustomed to view the life of the peasants to see how their misery is connected with our pleasures, and there you are.

Mitrofan.

But the remedy is not to ruin our own lives.

Stephen.

Isn't it extraordinary how Mitrofan Dmitrich and I, standing at opposite poles, agree on some points? Those are my exact words : not to ruin our own lives.

Boris.

It's perfectly simple. You both want a pleasant life, and so you want to adopt a plan of living that will ensure it. You (*turning to* Stephen) would like to preserve present conditions, and Mitrofan Dmitrich wants new ones.

(Luba *speaks under her breath to* Tonia. Tonia *goes to the piano and plays a Chopin Nocturne. All are silent.*)

Stephen.

That is beautiful. That solves all problems.

BORIS.

It only obscures them, and delays their solution.

> (*During the music enter silently* MARIE IVANOVNA *and the* PRINCESS. *They sit down and listen. Before the end of the Nocturne carriage bells are heard.*)

LUBA.

Oh, that is auntie !

> (*Goes to meet her. Music continues. Enter* ALEXANDRA IVANOVNA *and a* LAWYER *and* FATHER GERASIM *with his pectoral cross. All present rise.*)

FATHER GERASIM.

Pray continue.   It is very pleasant.

> (*The* PRINCESS *and* FATHER VASILY *go up to him and ask his blessing.*)

ALEXANDRA.

I have done what I said I would. I found Father Gerasim and persuaded him to come with me. He is going to Kursk. So I have done my part. And here is the lawyer. He has the papers all ready to sign.

MARIE.

Would you not like to have some luncheon ?
(*The* LAWYER *lays his papers on the table and goes.*)
I am very grateful to Father Gerasim.

FATHER GERASIM.

What else could I do ?   It was not on my way,
but my Christian duty bade me come.

> (PRINCESS *whispers to the young
> people.   They all talk among them-
> selves, and go out on the veranda,
> except* BORIS.   FATHER VASILY *rises
> to go.*)

FATHER GERASIM.

Stay with us.   You as a spiritual father, and
the pastor here, may derive some benefit and be
of use.   Stay, if Marie Ivanovna does not object.

MARIE.

Oh no.   Father Vasily is like one of the family
to me.   I consulted him as well, but being young,
he lacks authority.

FATHER GERASIM.

Undoubtedly, undoubtedly.

ALEXANDRA

(*approaching him*). Now, you see, Father Gerasim, you are the only one that can help us and persuade him to see reason. He is a clever man and a learned man ; but you know yourself, learning can only do harm. He does not see clearly somehow. He persists in saying that the Christian command is to have no possessions. But is that possible ?

FATHER GERASIM.

It is all a snare, intellectual pride, self-will. The fathers of the Church have settled that question adequately. But how did it all come about ?

MARIE.

To be quite frank with you, I must say that when we married he was indifferent to religious questions, and we lived the first twenty years of our life happily. Then he began to think about these things. His sister may, perhaps, have influenced him, or his reading. But at any rate he began to think, to read the Gospel, and then all at once he became very pious, going to church, visiting monks, and then he suddenly stopped all that and changed his life completely. Now he does everything for himself, he permits none of the servants to do anything for him, and, worst of all, he is giving away all his property. Yesterday he gave away

his forest and the land attached to it. I am afraid.
I have seven children. Do talk to him. I'll go
and ask whether he will see you. (*Exit.*)

FATHER GERASIM.

Yes, nowadays, many are leaving the Church.
What about the property? Does it belong to him
or his wife?

ALEXANDRA.

It is his own. That is the worst of it.

FATHER GERASIM.

And what is his rank?

PRINCESS.

Not a high one. I think he is a captain. He
has been in the army.

FATHER GERASIM.

Many are leaving the Church nowadays. In
Odessa there was a lady who became infatuated
with spiritualism, and she began to do a lot of
harm. But finally God prevailed, and brought
her again within the Church.

PRINCESS.

Now, father, you must understand. My son is
going to marry their daughter. I have given my

consent. But the girl is used to a life of luxury, and she must have means of her own so that the entire burden may not fall upon my son. I must say he works hard, and he is a remarkable young man.

(*Enter* MARIE IVANOVNA *and* NICHOLAS IVANOVICH.)

NICHOLAS.

How do you do, Princess? How do you do? Pardon me—I do not know your name (*to* FATHER GERASIM).

FATHER GERASIM.

Do you not wish for a blessing?

NICHOLAS.

No, I do not.

FATHER GERASIM.

I am Gerasim Feodorovich. Pleased to meet you. (FOOTMAN *brings refreshments and wine.*) It is fine weather, and very favourable for harvesting.

NICHOLAS.

I understand you have come on the invitation of Alexandra Ivanovna to convince me of my errors, and to lead me into the right way. If

7 a

that is the case, do not let us beat about the bush
Let us come to the point. I do not deny that
disagree with the teaching of the Church. I use
to believe in it, but I have ceased to do so. Never
theless, I long with my whole soul to be in har
mony with the truth, and if you can show it t
me, I will accept it without hesitation.

FATHER GERASIM.

How can you say you do not believe the teach
ing of the Church ? What are we to believe i
not the Church ?

NICHOLAS.

God, and His law, given to us in the Gospel.

FATHER GERASIM.

The Church instructs us in that very law.

NICHOLAS.

If that were so, I would believe the Church
But the Church teaches the very opposite.

FATHER GERASIM.

The Church cannot teach the opposite, for it i
founded by our Lord. It is said, " I give you the
power, and the Gates of Hell shall not prevai
against it."

NICHOLAS.

That refers to something quite different. But, supposing Christ did found a church, how do I know that it is *your* Church?

FATHER GERASIM.

Because it is said, "Where two or three are gathered together in My name——"

NICHOLAS.

That does not apply either, and does not prove anything.

FATHER GERASIM.

How can you renounce the Church, when the Church alone possesses grace?

NICHOLAS.

I did not renounce the Church until I was wholly convinced that it supports all that is contrary to Christianity.

FATHER GERASIM.

The Church cannot err, because she alone possesses the truth. Those err who leave her. The Church is sacred.

NICHOLAS.

But I have told you I do not admit that, because the Gospel says, " Ye shall know them by their fruits." And I perceive that the Church gives her sanction to oath-taking and murder and executions.

FATHER GERASIM.

The Church admits and consecrates the powers instituted by God.

> (*During the conversation enter one by one* LUBA, LISA, STEPHEN, TONIA, *and* BORIS, *who sit or stand and listen.*)

NICHOLAS.

I know that not only killing but anger is forbidden by the Gospel. And the Church gives its blessing to the army. The Gospel says, "Do not swear," and the Church administers oaths. The Gospel says——

FATHER GERASIM.

Excuse me—when Pilate said, "I ask you in the name of the living God," Christ accepted the oath, and said, "Yes, that I am."

NICHOLAS.

Oh, what are you saying? That is simply ridiculous!

FATHER GERASIM.

That is why the Church does not permit individuals to interpret the Gospel. She would preserve men from error, and she cares for them as a mother for her children. She gives them an interpretation befitting the powers of their mind. No! Allow me to finish. The Church does not give her children a burden heavier than they can bear. She requires only that they fulfil the commandments. Love, do not kill, do not steal, do not commit adultery.

NICHOLAS.

Yes. Do not kill me, do not steal from me what I have stolen. We have all robbed the people, have stolen their land, and then we instituted the law against stealing. And the Church sanctions it all.

FATHER GERASIM.

That is all a snare, mere spiritual pride speaking in you. You want to show off your intellect.

NICHOLAS.

Not at all! I merely ask you, how, according to the law of Christ, am I to behave now, when I have recognized the sin of robbing the people and appropriating their land? What must I do? Go on holding my land, exploiting the labour of the starving peasants, just for *this*? (*He points to the servant who is bringing in lunch and wine.*) Or am I to give back the land to those who have been robbed by my ancestors?

FATHER GERASIM.

You must act as a son of the Church should act. You have a family, children, and must bring them up as befits their station.

NICHOLAS.

Why must I?

FATHER GERASIM.

Because God has placed you in that station. And if you want to do charitable acts, then perform them by giving away part of your fortune, and by visiting the poor.

NICHOLAS.

Then why was it said that the rich man could not enter the kingdom of heaven?

FATHER GERASIM.

It was said, if he desired to be perfect.

NICHOLAS.

But I do want to be perfect. It is said in the Gospel, "Be ye perfect, even as your Father in heaven is perfect."

FATHER GERASIM.

But one must understand to what it applies.

Nicholas.

That is exactly what I am trying to understand, and all that was said in the Sermon on the Mount is simple and clear.

Father Gerasim.

It is all spiritual pride.

Nicholas.

Why pride, if it is said that what is hidden from the wise shall be revealed to babes?

Father Gerasim.

It will be revealed to the humble, not to the proud.

Nicholas.

But who is proud? Is it I, who think that I am like the rest, and therefore must live like the rest, live by my labour, and in the same poverty as all my brothers, or is it they who consider themselves apart from the rest, as the priests who think they know the whole truth, and cannot err, and interpret the words of Christ to suit themselves?

Father Gerasim

(*offended*). I beg your pardon, Nicholas Ivanovich, I have not come to argue as to who is right. I did not come to be lectured. I complied with the wish of Alexandra Ivanovna, and came to have a talk. But you appear to know everything better than I ; the conversation had better cease. But I beseech you for the last time, in the name of God, to reconsider the matter. You are terribly wrong, and will lose your own soul.

MARIE.

Won't you come and have something to eat ?

FATHER GERASIM.

Thank you very much. (*Accepts.*)

(*Exit with* ANNA IVANOVNA.)

MARIE

(*to* FATHER VASILY). What is the result of your talk ?

FATHER VASILY.

Well, my opinion is that Nicholas Ivanovich spoke truly, and Father Gerasim brought no arguments against what he said.

PRINCESS.

He was not allowed to speak. And then he did not like it. It became a sort of wordy tournament, with everybody listening. He withdrew out of modesty.

BORIS.

It was not at all from modesty.   Everything he said was false, and he obviously had nothing more to say.

PRINCESS.

Oh, I see.   With your usual fickleness you are beginning to agree with Nicholas Ivanovich.   If those are your opinions you ought not to marry.

BORIS.

I only say that truth is truth.   I cannot help saying it.

PRINCESS.

You are the last person who ought to speak like that.

BORIS.

Why ?

PRINCESS.

Because you are poor, and have nothing to give away.   However, the whole affair is no concern of ours.   (*Exit.*)

> (*After her all except* NICHOLAS *and* MARIE IVANOVNA *go out.*)

NICHOLAS

(*sits deep in thought and smiles meditatively*). Masha, what is all this about ?   Why did you ask that miserable, misguided man to come here? Why should that noisy woman and this priest take part in the most intimate questions of our life? Couldn't we settle all our affairs between ourselves?

MARIE.

But what can I do if you wish to leave our children with nothing? I cannot sit still and let you do that. You know it is not greed—I do not want anything for myself.

NICHOLAS.

I know, I know. I trust you. But the misfortune is that you do not believe. I don't mean that you don't believe the truth. I know you see it ; but you cannot bring yourself to trust it. You do not trust the truth, and you do not trust me. You would rather trust the crowd— the Princess and the rest.

MARIE.

I trust you ; I have always trusted you. But when you want to make our children beggars——

NICHOLAS.

That proves that you do not trust me. Do you imagine I have not struggled and have not had fears? But now I am perfectly convinced, not only that it can be done, but must be done, and that this is the only right thing to do for the children. You always say that if it were not for the children you would follow me. And I say that if it were not for the children you might go on living as you do. We should only be injuring ourselves. As it is we injure them.

MARIE.

But what can I do if I don't understand?

NICHOLAS.

And I—what am I to do? I know why you sent for that poor creature dressed up in his cassock and his cross, and I know why Aline brought the lawyer. You want me to transfer the estate to your name. I cannot do that. You know I have loved you during the twenty years we have been married. I love you, and I have every wish for your welfare, and that is why I cannot sign that transfer. If I am to make over the estate, then it must be to those from whom it came—the peasants. I cannot give it to you. I must give it to them. I am glad the lawyer has come. I must do it.

MARIE.

This is dreadful! Why are you so cruel? If you think it a sin to hold property, give it to me. (*Weeps.*)

NICHOLAS.

You do not know what you are saying. If I gave it to you I could not go on living with you. I should have to go away. I cannot continue to live in these conditions, and see the peasants squeezed dry, whether it is in your name or mine. I cannot see them put in prison. So choose.

MARIE.

How cruel you are! This is not Christianity; it is wicked. I cannot live as you want me to do. I cannot take things from my children to give to strangers, and for that you would forsake me! Well, go. I see that you no longer love me, and, indeed, I know the reason.

NICHOLAS.

Very well, I will sign it. But, Masha, you are asking the impossible of me. (*Goes to the table and signs.*) It is you who desired that. I cannot live so. (*Rushes away holding his head.*)

MARIE

(*calling*). Luba! Aline! (*They enter.*) He has signed—and gone. What am I to do? He said he would go away, and he will. Go to him.

LUBA.

He is gone.

ACT III.

SCENE I.

Scene is laid in Moscow. Large room, and in it a carpenter's bench, a table with papers, a bookcase. Boards lean against and cover the mirror and the pictures. NICHOLAS IVANOVICH *is working at the bench; a* CARPENTER *is planing.*

NICHOLAS

(*taking a finished board from the bench*). Is that all right ?

CARPENTER

(*adjusts the plane*). It's not up to much. Go at it ! Don't be afraid. Like that.

NICHOLAS.

I wish I could, but I cannot manage it.

CARPENTER.

But why do you go in for carpentering, sir ? There are so many in our trade now, you can't make a living at it.

NICHOLAS

(*continues working*). I am ashamed to live in idleness.

CARPENTER.

But that's your lot in life, sir. God has given you property.

NICHOLAS.

That is just the point. I do not believe God gave anything of the kind. Men have amassed goods that they have taken from their brothers.

CARPENTER

(*wondering*). That may all be very true. But still you need not work.

NICHOLAS.

I understand that it seems strange to you that in this house, where there is so much superfluity, I still wish to earn my living.

CARPENTER

(*laughing*). Well, that's just like you gentlemen. There's nothing you don't want to do. Now just smooth off that plank.

NICHOLAS.

Perhaps you will not believe me and will laugh at me when I say that I used to live that way and was not ashamed of it, but now that I believe the teaching of Christ, that we are all brothers, I am ashamed to live that life.

CARPENTER.

If you are ashamed give away your property.

NICHOLAS.

I wanted to, but I did not succeed. I have handed it over to my wife.

A VOICE

(*from outside*).   Father, may I come in?

NICHOLAS.

Of course you may!   You may always come in.

(*Enter* LUBA.)

LUBA.

Good-morning, Yakov.

CARPENTER.

Good-morning, miss.

LUBA

(*to her father*).   Boris has left for the regiment. I'm so afraid he will do or say something he ought not to.   What do you think?

NICHOLAS.

What can I think?   He will act according to his conscience.

Luba.

But that's awful. He has only such a short time to serve now, and he may go and ruin his life.

Nicholas.

He did well in not coming to me. He knows I cannot tell him anything beyond what he knows himself. He told me himself that he asked for his discharge because he saw that there could not be a more lawless, cruel, brutal occupation than that which is based on murder. And that there is nothing more humiliating than to obey implicitly any man who happens to be his superior in rank. He knows all this.

Luba.

That is precisely what I'm afraid of. He knows of all that and he'll be sure to do something.

Nicholas.

His conscience, that God within him, must decide that. If he had come to me I should have advised him only one thing, not to act on the dictates of reason, but only when his whole being demanded it. There's nothing worse than that. There was I, desiring to do Christ's bidding, which is to leave father, wife, children—and follow Him. And I was on the point of going. And

how did that end ?   It ended by my coming back
and living in town, with you, in luxury.   That
was because I wanted to do something beyond my
strength, and it ended in placing me in a stupid
and humiliating position.   I want to live simply—
to work—and in these surroundings, with footmen
and hall porters, it becomes a pose.   There, I see
Yakov Nikanorovich is laughing at me.

CARPENTER.

Why should I laugh ?   You pay me—you give
me tea—I am very grateful to you.

LUBA.

Don't you think I had better go to him, father?

NICHOLAS.

My darling, I know how hard it is for you—
how terrible !   But you ought not to be frightened.
I am a man who understands life.   No harm can
come of it.   All that seems to you bad really
brings joy to the heart.   You must understand
that a man who chooses that path has had to make
a choice.   There are circumstances in which the
scales balance evenly between God and the devil.
And at that moment God's greatest work is being
done.   Any interference from without is very
dangerous, and only brings suffering.   It is as

though a man were making a great effort to bear down the scale, and the touch of a finger may break his back.

LUBA.

But why suffer?

NICHOLAS.

It is the same thing as though a mother should say, "Why suffer?" But a child cannot be born without pain. And so it is with spiritual birth. I can only say one thing—Boris is a true Christian, and therefore free. And if you cannot be like him, if you cannot believe God as he does, then believe God through him.

MARIE.

(*outside the door*). May I come in?

NICHOLAS.

Certainly—always. Quite a meeting here to-day.

MARIE.

Our priest has come—Vasily Ermilovich. He is on his way to the bishop to resign his cure.

NICHOLAS.

Not really. Is he here? Luba, call him. He will certainly want to see me.

(*Exit* LUBA.)

Marie.

I came to tell you about Vania. He is behaving so badly and will not study, and I am sure he will not pass. I have tried to talk to him but he is impertinent.

Nicholas.

Masha—you know I do not sympathize with your mode of life and your ideas of education. It is an awful question whether I have the right to look on and see my children ruined.

Marie.

Then you must offer a definite substitute. What do you propose?

Nicholas.

I cannot say—I can only tell you that the first thing is to get rid of this corrupting luxury.

Marie.

And make peasants of them! That I cannot agree to.

Nicholas.

Then do not ask me. All that upsets you now is inevitable. (*Enter* Father Vasily *and embraces* Nicholas Ivanovich.) Then you have really done it?

Father Vasily.

I cannot go on any longer !

Nicholas.

I did not expect it would come so soon.

Father Vasily.

It had to come. In my vocation one cannot remain indifferent. I had to confess, to administer the sacrament ; how could I, knowing it to be false ?

Nicholas.

And what will happen now ?

Father Vasily.

I am going to the bishop to be examined. I am afraid I shall be exiled to the Solavetsky Monastery. I thought at one time of running away and going abroad, of asking you to help me, but then I gave up the idea. It would be cowardly. The only thing is—my wife——

Nicholas.

Where is she ?

Father Vasily.

She has gone to her father. My mother-in-law came and took away our son. That hurt. I wanted so much—— (*He stops, hardly restraining his tears.*)

NICHOLAS.

Well, God help you. Are you staying here with us ?

(*Enter* ALEXANDRA IVANOVNA *with a letter.*)

ALEXANDRA.

A special messenger has brought this for you, Nicholas Ivanovich. How do you do, Father Vasily ?

FATHER VASILY.

I am no longer Father Vasily, Alexandra Ivanovna.

ALEXANDRA.

Really ! Why ?

FATHER VASILY.

I have discovered that we do not believe in the right way.

ALEXANDRA.

Oh dear, oh dear, how sinful ! You are a good man, but what errors you do fall into. It is all Nicholas Ivanovich's doing.

FATHER VASILY.

Not Nicholas Ivanovich's, but Christ's.

ALEXANDRA.

Oh, stop, stop ! Why leave the fold of the

Orthodox Church ?   I know you mean well, but
you are ruining your own soul.

NICHOLAS

(*to himself*).   I expected this.   What am I to
do ?

ALEXANDRA.

What is it ?

NICHOLAS

(*reading*).   It is from the Princess.   This is
what she writes : " Boris has refused to serve and
has been arrested.   You have been his ruin.   It is
your duty to save him.   He is at the Kroutitsk
Barracks."   Yes, I must go to him, if only they
will let me see him.   (*He takes off his apron, puts
his coat on, and goes out.*)   (*Exit all.*)

SCENE II.

Office.   A CLERK *sitting.*   SENTRY *pacing up
and down at opposite door.*

(*Enter* GENERAL *with his* AIDE-DE-
CAMP.   CLERK *jumps up.*   SENTRY
salutes.)

GENERAL.

Where is the Colonel ?

CLERK.

He was asked to go to see the recruit, your
excellency.

General.

Very well.   Ask him to come here.

Clerk.

Yes, your excellency.

General.

What are you copying there ?   The deposition
of the recruit ?

Clerk.

Yes, your excellency.

General.

Give it to me.

(CLERK *gives it and goes out.*)

General

(*giving paper to* AIDE-DE-CAMP).   Read it, please.

AIDE-DE-CAMP

(*reading*).   "To the questions which were put
to me : (1) Why I refused to take the oath ; (2)
Why I refused to carry out the demands of the
Government ; and (3) What made me utter words
offensive not only to the military body, but to the
highest authority, I answer, to the first question,
I will not take the oath because I profess the
teaching of Christ.   In His teaching Christ clearly
forbids it, as in the Gospel (Matt. v. 33-37, and
the Epistle of James, v. 12)."

GENERAL.

There they are, discussing and putting their own interpretations on it.

AIDE-DE-CAMP

(*continuing*). "It is said in the Gospel (Matt. v. 37), 'Let your communication be, Yea, yea; Nay, nay: for whatsoever is more than these cometh of evil,' and (Jas. v. 12), 'But above all things, my brethren, swear not, neither by heaven, neither by the earth, neither by any other oath; but let your yea be yea; and your nay, nay; lest ye fall into condemnation.'

"But even if there were not such explicit prohibition of swearing in the Gospel, I would not swear to fulfil the will of men, for according to Christ's teaching I am bound to fulfil the will of God, which may not coincide with the will of men."

GENERAL.

There they are, discussing! If I had my way, such things would not occur.

AIDE-DE-CAMP

(*reading*). "And I refuse to comply with the demands of men calling themselves the government because——"

GENERAL.

What impudence!

AIDE-DE-CAMP

(*continuing*). " —because these demands are criminal
and wicked.   I am required to enter the army, to
be prepared and instructed how to murder.   This
is forbidden by the Old as well as by the New
Testament, and, moreover, by my conscience.   As
to the third question——"

> (*Enter* COLONEL *with* CLERK.
> GENERAL *shakes hands with* COLONEL.)

COLONEL.

You are reading the deposition ?

GENERAL.

Yes.   Unpardonably impudent.   Continue.

AIDE-DE-CAMP

(*reading*).   " As to the third question, what induced
me to speak offensively to the Council.   I answer,
that I was led by my desire to serve God and to
denounce shams which are perpetrated in His
name.   This desire I hope to preserve while I
live.   That is why——"

GENERAL.

Oh, enough of that rubbish !   The question is,
how to root it all out, and prevent him from corrupting our men.   (*To* COLONEL) Have you
spoken to him ?

8

Colonel.

I have been talking to him all this time. I tried to appeal to his conscience, to make him understand that he was only making matters worse for himself and that he would not achieve anything by such methods. I spoke to him about his family. He is very excited, but he stuck to his words.

General.

It is idle to say much to him. We are soldiers; men of actions, not words. Have him brought here.

(*Exeunt* AIDE-DE-CAMP *and* CLERK.)

General

(*sitting down*). No, Colonel. You were wrong. Such fellows must be dealt with in quite another fashion. Strong measures are needed to cut off the offending member. One foul sheep ruins the whole flock. Sentimentality has no place here. His being a prince and having a mother and a *fiancée* does not concern us. There is a soldier before us and we must fulfil the will of the Tsar.

Colonel.

I only thought it would be easier to influence him by persuasion.

GENERAL.

Not at all. Firmness, only firmness. I had a case like this once before. He must be made to feel that he is nothing, that he is a grain of sand under the wheel of a chariot, and that he cannot impede its progress.

COLONEL.

Well, we can try.

GENERAL

(*beginning to get angry*). It is not a question of trying. I have nothing to try. I have served my sovereign for forty-four years, have given and am giving my life to the service, and suddenly a boy comes and wants to teach me, and quotes Bible texts. Let him talk that nonsense to the priests. To me he is either a soldier or a prisoner. That's the end of it.

> (*Enter* BORIS *under escort of two* SOLDIERS. AIDE-DE-CAMP *follows him in.*)

GENERAL

(*pointing to* BORIS *with his finger*). Place him there.

BORIS.

No necessity whatever to "place" me anywhere. I will stand or sit where I please, for as to your authority over me, I do not——

GENERAL.

Silence ! You don't recognize my authority—
I'll make you recognize it !

BORIS

(*sits down*). How wrong of you to shout like
that !

GENERAL.

Lift him up and make him stand !

(SOLDIERS *raise* BORIS *up*.)

BORIS.

That you can do. You can kill me, but you
cannot force me to obey you.

GENERAL.

Silence, I say ! Listen to what I say to you.

BORIS.

I do not in the least wish to hear what you say.

GENERAL.

He is mad. He must be sent to the hospital
to test his sanity. That's the only thing to do
with him.

COLONEL.

We have orders to send him to the Gendarmerie
Department to be questioned.

GENERAL.

Very well—do so. But put him into uniform.

COLONEL.

He refuses to wear it.

GENERAL.

Then tie his hands and feet. (*To* BORIS) Now listen to what I am going to tell you. It is a matter of perfect indifference to me what becomes of you. But for your own sake I would advise you to think it over. You will only rot in the fortress, and be of no use to any one. Give it up. You were excited, and so was I. (*Slapping him on the shoulder.*) Go—take your oath and drop all that nonsense. (*To the* AIDE-DE-CAMP) Is the priest here? (*To* BORIS) Well? (BORIS *is silent.*) Why don't you answer? I assure you I'm advising you for your own good. The weakest goes to the wall. You can keep your own ideas and merely serve your time. We won't be hard on you. Well?

BORIS.

I have nothing more to say. I have said everything.

GENERAL.

Just now you said that there were such and such verses in the Gospel. Surely the priests

know that? You'd better talk that over with
the priest, and then think it over. That's surely
the best way. Good-bye. I hope to meet you
again and be able to congratulate you on your
entrance into the service of the Tsar. Send the
priest here.

(*Exeunt* GENERAL *with* COLONEL
and AIDE-DE-CAMP.)

BORIS

(*to* SOLDIERS *and* CLERK). You see how they talk.
They are perfectly aware themselves that they are
deceiving you. Don't give in to them. Throw
down your arms. Go away. Let them flog you
to death in their disciplinary battalions. Even
that is better than to be the slaves of these
impostors!

CLERK.

No, that's impossible. How can we get on
without the army? It is impossible.

BORIS.

We must not reason in that way. We must
do just as God desires. And God desires us to——

SOLDIER.

Then why do they call it the " Christ-serving
Army " ?

BORIS.

That is not said anywhere.   It's the invention of these impostors.

SOLDIER.

How so ?   The bishops must know.

(*Enter* POLICE OFFICER *with* STENOGRAPHER.)

POLICE OFFICER

(*to* CLERK).   Is Prince Cheremshanov the recruit here ?

CLERK.

Yes, sir.   There he is.

POLICE OFFICER.

Please step this way.   Are you the Prince Boris Cheremshanov who refused to take the oath ?

BORIS.

I am he.

(OFFICER *sits down and motions to a seat opposite himself.*)

POLICE OFFICER.

Please sit down.

BORIS.

I think there's no use in our talking.

POLICE OFFICER.

I don't agree.   To you at any rate it may be

of advantage. You see, I have been informed that you refused military service and refused to take the oath, which raises the suspicion that you belong to the revolutionary party. And this I have to investigate. If this is true, then we must remove you from military service, and either put you in prison or exile you, according to the extent of your participation in the revolutionary movement. Otherwise we leave you to the military authorities. Please note that I have told you everything quite frankly, and I trust you will show the same confidence in talking to us.

Boris.

In the first place I cannot have any confidence in those who wear that (*pointing to the uniform*). In the second place, your very office is of such a nature that I cannot respect it, but, on the contrary, despise it from my heart. But I will not refuse to answer your questions. What is it you want to know ?

Police Officer.

First, please, your name, rank, and religious faith.

Boris.

You know all that, so that I will not answer. Only one of those questions is of any importance to me.   I do *not* belong to the so-called Orthodox Church.

POLICE OFFICER.

Then what is your religion?

BORIS.

I cannot define it.

POLICE OFFICER.

Still——

BORIS.

Let us say Christian, founded on the Sermon on the Mount.

POLICE OFFICER.

Take that down.

(STENOGRAPHER *writes*.)

POLICE OFFICER

(*to* BORIS).   But you acknowledge that you belong to some state, some class?

BORIS.

I do not admit that.   I consider myself a man, a servant of God.

POLICE OFFICER.

But why do you not recognize your allegiance to the Russian State?

BORIS.

Because I do not recognize the existence of any State.

8 a

Police Officer.

What do you mean when you say you do not recognize it ?   Do you want to destroy it ?

Boris.

Most certainly I do, and I work to that end.

Police Officer

(*to* Scribe).   Take that down.   (*To* Boris) By what means do you work ?

Boris.

By denouncing deceit and lies, and by spreading the truth.   Just now, the moment before you entered, I was telling these soldiers that they must not believe the deceit in which they are made to share.

Police Officer.

But beside these measures of denunciation and proselytizing, do you admit other means ?

Boris.

I not only exclude violence, but I consider it the greatest sin, and all underhand actions also.

Police Officer

(*to* Scribe).   Take it down.   (*To* Boris) Very good. Now allow me to ask you about your acquaintances, your friends.   Do you know Ivashenkov ?

BORIS.

No.

POLICE OFFICER.

And Klein?

BORIS.

I have heard of him, but I have never seen him.

(*Enter* CHAPLAIN.)

POLICE OFFICER.

Well, I think that is all. I consider that you are not a dangerous person. You do not concern our department. I hope you will soon be released. Good-day. (*Shakes hands.*)

BORIS.

There is one thing I should like to say to you. Excuse me, but I cannot resist saying it. Why have you chosen such a bad and wicked calling? I would advise you to leave it.

POLICE OFFICER

(*smiling*). Thank you for your advice: I have my reasons. Now, father, I'll give up my place to you.

(*The* PRIEST, *an old man with cross and Testament, steps forward. The* SCRIBE *advances to receive his blessing.*)

Chaplain

(*to* Boris). Why do you grieve your superiors and refuse to perform the duty of a Christian by serving your Tsar and country?

Boris

(*smiling*). It is precisely because I wish to perform the duties of a Christian that I do not wish to be a soldier.

Chaplain.

Why do you not wish it? It is written, "Lay down your life for your friends." That is the part of a true Christian.

Boris.

Yes, to lay down your own, but not to take the life of others. To give up my life is just what I wish.

Chaplain.

You judge wrongly, young man. And what did Jesus Christ say to the soldiers?

Boris

(*smiling*). That only proves that even in His time soldiers plundered, and He forbade them to do so.

Chaplain.

Well—why do you refuse to take the oath?

Boris.

You know it is forbidden in the Gospel.

Chaplain.

Not at all. How was it that when Pilate said, "In the name of God I ask you, are you the Christ?" our Lord Jesus Christ answered, "I am He." That proves an oath is not forbidden.

Boris.

Are you not ashamed to say that, you, an old man?

Chaplain.

I advise you not to be obstinate. It is not for us to change the world. Take the oath, and have done with it. As for what is sin and what is not sin, leave that for the Church to decide.

Boris.

Leave it to you? Are you not afraid to take such a weight of sin upon your soul?

Chaplain.

What sin? I have always been true to the faith in which I was educated. I have been a priest now for over thirty years; there can be no sin upon my soul.

Boris.

Then whose is the sin of deceiving so many

people ? You know what *their* heads are full of. (*Points to the* SENTRY.)

CHAPLAIN.

That, young man, is not for us to judge. Our duty is to obey our superiors.

BORIS.

Leave me alone. I pity you, and what you say disgusts me. If you were like that General it would not be so bad. But you come with cross and Bible to try to persuade me in the name of Christ to deny Christ. Go—go ! (*Excitedly.*) Go. Take me away where I shall see no one. I am tired—I am terribly tired.

CHAPLAIN.

Well, good-bye.

(*Enter* AIDE-DE-CAMP. BORIS *retires to back of scene.*)

AIDE-DE-CAMP.

Well ?

CHAPLAIN.

Great stubbornness. Great insubordination.

AIDE-DE-CAMP.

He has not consented to take the oath and to serve ?

CHAPLAIN.

Not in the least.

AIDE-DE-CAMP.

Then I shall have to take him to the hospital.

CHAPLAIN.

To make out that he is ill. Of course that's the best way ; otherwise his example might be bad for the rest.

AIDE-DE-CAMP.

He will be examined in the ward for mental ailments. These are my orders.

CHAPLAIN.

Of course. Good-day. (*Exit.*)

AIDE-DE-CAMP

(*approaching* BORIS). Please come with me. I am ordered to escort you.

BORIS.

Where to ?

AIDE-DE-CAMP.

Just for a time, to the hospital, where you will be more comfortable, and will have leisure to think the matter over.

BORIS.

I have thought it over for some time. But let us go. (*Exeunt.*)

Scene III.

Reception-room in the Hospital. Head Physician *and* House Surgeon *and* Patients *in hospital dress.* Warders *in blouses.*

Sick Officer.

I tell you, you simply make me worse. There were times when I felt quite well.

Head Physician.

Don't get so excited. I am quite willing to discharge you, but you know yourself that it is unsafe for you to be at liberty. If I knew that you would be taken care of——

Sick Officer.

You think I shall begin to drink again. Oh no! I've learned my lesson. Every additional day spent here is simply killing me. You do just the contrary to what (*over-excited*) should be done. You are cruel. It is all very well for you——

Head Physician.

Calm yourself. (*Makes a sign to* Warders *who approach the* Officer *from behind.*)

SICK OFFICER.

It's all very well for you to talk when you are free. But how do you think I feel here in the company of lunatics? (*To* WARDERS) Why are you coming so near to me? Get away!

HEAD PHYSICIAN.

I beg you to be calm.

SICK OFFICER.

And I beg, I insist on my discharge. (*Shrieks, rushes at* DOCTOR. WARDERS *seize him—a struggle— they lead him away.*)

HOUSE SURGEON.

Same thing all over again. He was on the point of striking you.

HEAD PHYSICIAN.

Alcoholic subject, and there's nothing to be done for him. Still there is some improvement.

(*Enter* AIDE-DE-CAMP.)

AIDE-DE-CAMP.

Good-morning.

HEAD PHYSICIAN.

Good-morning.

AIDE-DE-CAMP.

I have brought you a very interesting case. A certain Prince Cheremshanov was to do his military service, and refused on the ground of the Gospel. He was handed over to the police, but they found him outside their jurisdiction, and decided it was not a political case. The chaplain talked to him, but without the slightest effect.

HEAD PHYSICIAN

(*laughing*). And as usual you bring him to us as the last resort. Well, let's have a look at him.

(*Exit* HOUSE SURGEON.)

AIDE-DE-CAMP.

They say he is a well-educated fellow, and that he's engaged to a rich girl. It is very strange. I must say the hospital is exactly the right place for him.

HEAD PHYSICIAN.

It must be a case of mania—— (BORIS *is brought in.*) Good-morning. Please sit down. We'll have a little talk. (*To the others*) Leave us alone.

(*Exeunt all save* BORIS *and* PHYSICIAN.)

BORIS.

I would like to ask you, if you are going to shut me up somewhere, to do it as quickly as possible and let me have a rest.

HEAD PHYSICIAN.

Excuse me : I must comply with the regulations. I will merely put a few questions to you. How do you feel ? From what are you suffering ?

BORIS.

There's nothing the matter with me. I am perfectly well.

HEAD PHYSICIAN.

Yes ; but your conduct is different from the conduct of others.

BORIS.

I am acting according to the dictates of my conscience.

HEAD PHYSICIAN.

You have refused to perform your military duty. What is your motive ?

BORIS.

I am a Christian, and therefore cannot kill.

HEAD PHYSICIAN.

But is it not necessary to protect the country

from foreign enemies, and restrain from evil those who disturb the peace within ?

BORIS.

The country is not attacked by any enemies, and as for disturbers of the peace within her borders, there are more of those within the Government than among the people towards whom the Government uses violence.

HEAD PHYSICIAN.

What do you mean by that ?

BORIS.

I mean that the chief cause of evil—alcohol—is sold by the Government ; a false religious creed is spread by the Government ; and the very military service, such as I am required to perform, and which is the principal means of corruption in the country, is required by the Government.

HEAD PHYSICIAN.

Then, according to your views, Government and State are unnecessary.

BORIS.

I do not know ; but I am quite sure I must not participate in these evils.

Head Physician.

But what will become of the world?   We are given a mind with which to look ahead.

Boris.

Yes, and we are also given common sense to see that the organization of society shall not be founded on violence, but on love, and that the refusal of one man to participate in evil has nothing dangerous in it——

Head Physician.

Now please let me make an examination.   Will you kindly lie down?   (*Begins to examine him.*) Do you feel any pain here?

Boris.

No.

Head Physician.

Nor here?

Boris.

No.

Head Physician.

Breathe.   Now don't breathe.   Thank you. Now allow me.   (*Takes out a measure and measures his nose and his forehead.*)   Now be so kind as to shut your eyes and walk.

BORIS.

Aren't you ashamed to do all that ?

HEAD PHYSICIAN.

What ?

BORIS.

All these silly things. You know perfectly well that I'm all right, and have been sent here for refusing to take part in their wickedness, and as they had no arguments to offer in opposition to my truth, they pretend that they think me abnormal. And you aid them in that ! That is despicable and disgraceful. You'd better stop it.

HEAD PHYSICIAN.

Then you do not wish to walk ?

BORIS.

No, I do not. You may torment me as much as you like. That is your business. But I do not wish to help you in it. (*Vehemently*) Stop it, I say !

(HEAD PHYSICIAN *presses a button.*
Two WARDERS *enter.*)

HEAD PHYSICIAN.

Be calm, please. I quite understand that your

nerves are rather overstrained. Would you not like to go to your quarters?

(*Enter* House Surgeon.)

House Surgeon.
Visitors have come for Cheremshanov.

Boris.
Who are they?

House Surgeon.
Sarintsev and his daughter.

Boris.
I should like to see them.

Head Physician.
I have no objection. Ask them in. You may receive them here.

(*Enter* Nicholas Ivanovich *and* Luba. Princess Cheremshanova *puts her head into the door, saying,* " *Go in, I'll come later.*")

Luba
(*goes straight to* Boris, *takes his face between her hands, and kisses him*). Poor Boris!

Boris.
No, don't pity me. I feel so well—so happy.

I am so easy in my mind. (*To* NICHOLAS IVAN-
OVICH) How do you do ? (*Embraces him.*)

NICHOLAS.

I came to tell you something important. In the
first place, it is worse in such cases to overdo it
than to do too little ; in the second place, you
must act according to the Gospel, taking no thought
as to your future words and acts. When taken
before the authorities "think not what ye shall say,
for the Holy Ghost will teach you in that hour
what ye ought to say." The moment to act is not
when your reason dictates this or that, but only
when your whole being determines your action.

BORIS.

That's just what I did. I did not think I should
refuse to serve. But when I saw all this falsehood,
the emblem of justice, the documents, the police,
and the members of the Council smoking—I could
not help speaking as I did. It seemed a terrible
thing to do, but only till I began. Then all
became so simple and delightful.

(LUBA *sits weeping.*)

NICHOLAS.

Above all, do nothing for the sake of the praise
of men, or in order to please those whose esteem

you value. As for myself, I tell you honestly that if you took the oath this moment and entered the army, I would love and respect you no less; possibly even more than before, because it is not what is done in the world that is of value, but what is done within the soul.

BORIS.

That is certainly so, because if a thing is done within the soul, it will bring about a change in the world.

NICHOLAS.

Well, I have said what I had to say. Your mother is here, and she is quite broken-hearted. If you can do what she desires, do it. That is what I wanted to tell you.

> (*In the corridor frightful screaming of the lunatics. One lunatic bursts into the room.* WARDERS *follow and drag him away.*)

LUBA.

This is dreadful! And you will have to be here! (*Weeps.*)

BORIS.

This doesn't frighten me. Nothing frightens me now. I feel at peace. The only thing that I

fear is your attitude to all this. Help me—I'm
sure you will help me.

LUBA.

How can I be glad?

NICHOLAS.

Be glad! That is impossible. Neither am I
glad. I suffer for him and would willingly take
his place. But I am suffering, and yet I know that
it is for the best.

LUBA.

For the best! When will they let him go?

BORIS.

No one knows. I am not thinking about the
future; the present is joyful. And you could make
it still more so.

(*Enter* PRINCESS.)

PRINCESS.

I can wait no longer. (*To* NICHOLAS IVANOVICH)
Well, have you persuaded him? Are you willing,
Boris darling? You must know how I have
suffered. Thirty years of my life have been given
to you. To bring you up and be so proud of you,
and then when all is ready and finished, suddenly
to give up everything. Prison, disgrace! No,
Boris——

BORIS.

Listen, mother.

PRINCESS

(*to* NICHOLAS IVANOVICH). Why don't you say something? You have brought about his ruin, and you ought to persuade him. It's all very well for you. Luba, speak to him!

LUBA.

What can I do?

BORIS.

Mother, try to understand that some things are impossible. Just as it is impossible to fly, so it is impossible for me to serve in the army.

PRINCESS.

You only imagine you cannot! It's all nonsense. Others have served, and are serving now. You and Nicholas Ivanovich have invented a new Christian creed that is not Christian at all. It is a diabolical creed, that causes suffering to every one around you.

BORIS.

So it is written in the Gospel.

PRINCESS.

Nothing of that sort is said. And if it is, it's

simply stupid.   Boris darling, spare me!   (*Falls on his neck and sobs.*)   My whole life has been full of sorrow.   You have been my only gleam of gladness, and now you turn it into anguish.   Boris, have pity!

BORIS.

It is very, very painful to me, mother, but I cannot promise you that.

PRINCESS.

Do not refuse.   Say you will try!

NICHOLAS.

Say you will think it over, and do think it over.

BORIS.

Very well—I will do that.   But have pity on me, also, mother.   It is hard for me too.   (*Again desperate screams in a corridor.*)   I am in a lunatic asylum, you see, and I may lose my reason.

(*Enter* HEAD PHYSICIAN.)

HEAD PHYSICIAN.

Madame, this may have the worst results.   Your son is in a very excited state.   I think we had better consider the visit at an end.   The regular visiting day is Thursday before twelve.

PRINCESS.

Well, well, I will go. Good-bye, Boris. Only do think it over. Spare me, and on Thursday meet me with good news. (*Kisses him.*)

NICHOLAS

(*shaking hands with him*). Think it over, with God's help, as if to-morrow you were going to die. That is the only way to make the right decision. Good-bye.

BORIS

(*approaching* LUBA). What are you going to say to me?

LUBA.

What can I say? I cannot be untruthful. I do not understand why you torture yourself and others. I do not understand, and there is nothing I can say. (*Weeps.*)

(*They all go.*)

BORIS

(*alone*). Oh, how difficult, how difficult it is! God help me!

(*Enter* WARDERS *with hospital attire.*)

WARDER.

Will you please put this on?

BORIS

(*begins to change—then*). No, I will not!

(*They change his garments by force.*)

ACT IV.

Scene I.

Moscow. A year has passed since the third act. Big drawing-room with piano arranged for dancing party in Sarintsev's house. Footman *arranges flowers in front of piano. A Christmas tree.*

> (*Enter* Marie Ivanovna *in elegant silk dress, with* Alexandra Ivanovna.)

MARIE.

It isn't a ball. It is only a small dance. A party, as we used to say, for the young people. I can't let my children go out to dances and never give a party myself.

ALEXANDRA.

I'm afraid Nicholas will be displeased.

MARIE.

What can I do? (*To* Footman) Put it here. Heaven knows I do not want to grieve him. But I think he is less exacting now, on the whole.

ALEXANDRA.

Oh no! Only he does not talk about it. He seemed quite upset when he went to his room after dinner.

MARIE.

But what is to be done? what is to be done? We must all live. There are six children, and if I did not provide some amusement for them at home, Heaven knows what they would do. At any rate, I am happy about Luba.

ALEXANDRA.

Has he proposed?

MARIE.

Practically. He has spoken to her and she has accepted him.

ALEXANDRA.

That will be another awful blow for him.

MARIE.

But he knows. He cannot help knowing.

ALEXANDRA.

He does not like him.

MARIE

(*to* FOOTMAN). Put the fruit on the sideboard. Whom do you mean? Alexis Mikhailovich? Of course not, for he is the embodied negation of all his theories—a man of the world, nice, kind, agreeable. Oh, that awful nightmare of Boris Cheremshanov! How is he now?

ALEXANDRA.

Lisa has been to see him. He's still there. She says he has grown very thin, and the doctors are anxious about his life or reason.

MARIE.

He is a victim of his dreadful theories. His life ruined—to what end? It certainly was not my wish. (*Enter* PIANIST.) You have come to play for the dancing?

PIANIST.

Yes, I am the pianist.

MARIE.

Please sit down and wait. Will you have some tea?

PIANIST.

No, thank you. (*Goes to piano.*)

MARIE.

I never wished it. I was fond of Boris. But

of course he was no match for Luba, especially after taking up with Nicholas's ideas.

ALEXANDRA.

Still, his strength of conviction is extraordinary. What agony he has been through! They tell him that if he will not give in he must stay where he is or else be sent to the fortress, and he gives them but one answer. And Lisa says he's so happy, even merry.

MARIE.

Fanatic! Oh, there's Alexis Mikhailovich!

(*Enter the brilliant* ALEXIS MIKHAIL-OVICH STARKOVSKY *in evening dress.*)

STARKOVSKY.

I have come early. (*Kisses the hands of both ladies.*)

MARIE.

So much the better.

STARKOVSKY.

And Lubov Nicolaevna? She said she was going to dance a lot to make up for what she had missed. I volunteered to help her.

MARIE.

She is arranging the favours for the cotillon.

9

STARKOVSKY.

I'll go and help her.   May I ?

MARIE.

Certainly.

> (STARKOVSKY *turns to go, and meets* LUBA *coming toward him carrying a cushion on which are stars and ribbons.* LUBA *in evening dress, not low-necked.*)

LUBA.

Oh, there you are !   That's right.   Do help me.   There are two more cushions in the drawing-room, bring them here.   How do you do !   How do you do !

STARKOVSKY.

I am off !   (*Goes.*)

MARIE

(*to* LUBA).   Listen, Luba.   To-night our guests are sure to make insinuations and ask questions. May we announce it ?

LUBA.

No, mother, no.   Why ?   Let them ask.   It would grieve father.

MARIE.

But he must know, or at least guess.   And we

shall have to tell him sooner or later. I really think it is best to announce it to-night. It is a farcical secret.

LUBA.

No, no, mother—please! It would spoil the whole evening. No, don't!

MARIE.

Very well, as you like.

LUBA.

Or, anyhow, not till the end of the evening, just before supper. (*Calling out.*) Well, are you bringing them?

MARIE.

I will go and see to Natasha.

(*Exit with* ANNA IVANOVNA.)

STARKOVSKY

(*brings three cushions, the top one under his chin, and lets something drop*). Don't you trouble, Lubov Nicolaevna, I'll pick them up. I say, what a lot of favours you've got! The thing is to distribute them properly! Vania, come here.

(*Enter* VANIA, *carrying more favours.*)

VANIA.

That's the last of them.   Luba, Alexis Mikhailo-vich and I have got a bet on as to who will get most favours.

STARKOVSKY.

It's very easy for you.   You know everybody, so you are sure of theirs in advance.   I must win the girls before I can get any favours at all.   So I have a handicap of forty points, you see.

VANIA.

But you are grown up, and I'm only a boy.

STARKOVSKY.

I'm not very grown up, and so I am worse than a boy.

LUBA.

Vania, please go to my room and bring me the paste and my needle-case ; they're on the shelf. But for mercy's sake don't break the watch there.

VANIA

(*running off*).   I'll break everything.

STARKOVSKY

(*takes* LUBA's *hand*).   May I, Luba ?   I am so happy.   (*Kisses her hand.*)   The mazurka is mine, but that isn't enough.   There isn't time in the mazurka to say much, and I have a great deal to say. May I telegraph to my people and tell them you have accepted me and how happy I am?

LUBA.

Yes, you can do it to-night.

STARKOVSKY.

One word more. How will Nicholas Ivanovich take the news? Have you told him? Have you told him? Yes?

LUBA.

No, I have not, but I will. He will take it just as he takes everything now that concerns his family. He will say, "Do as you like." But in his heart he will be grieved.

STARKOVSKY.

Because I am not Cheremshanov—because I am a chamberlain, a marshal of nobility?

LUBA.

Yes. But I have tried to fight against myself— to deceive myself for his sake. And it is not because I do not love him that I do not follow his wishes, but because I cannot act a lie. And he says himself that one should not. I long to live my own life!

Starkovsky.

Life is the only truth there is. What has become of Cheremshanov ?

Luba

(*agitated*). Do not talk to me about him. I want to find fault with him even when he is suffering. I know it is because I am to blame about him. But one thing I do know: that there is such a thing as love—real love—and that I never had for him.

Starkovsky.

Do you really mean it, Luba ?

Luba.

You want me to say that it is you that I love with a real love ? I will not say that. I certainly love you . . . But it is a different kind of love. Neither of them is the real thing. If I could only put them both together . . .

Starkovsky.

Oh no, I'm quite content with mine. (*Kisses her hand.*) Luba !

Luba

(*moving from him*). No ; we must talk this over. You see, the guests are beginning to arrive.

(*Enter* COUNTESS *with* TONIA *and a younger* GIRL.)
Mother will be here directly.

COUNTESS.

We are the first then ?

STARKOVSKY.

Somebody must be first.   I offered to make an india-rubber lady to be the first arrival.

> (*Enter* STEPHEN *with* VANIA, *who brings the paste and needles.*)

STEPHEN

(*to* TONIA).   I hoped to see you last night at the Italian opera.

TONIA.

We were at my aunt's, sewing for the poor.

> (*Enter* STUDENTS, LADIES, *and* MARIE IVANOVNA.)

COUNTESS

(*to* MARIE IVANOVNA).   Shall we not see Nicholas Ivanovich ?

MARIE.

No; he never leaves his rooms.

STEPHEN.

How did Cheremshanov's affair end ?

MARIE.

He is still in the asylum, poor boy.

COUNTESS.

What obstinacy !

ONE OF THE GUESTS.

What an extraordinary delusion !   What good can come of it ?

STUDENT.

Take your partners for the quadrille, please !

> (*Claps his hands.   They take up their positions and dance.   Enter* ALEXANDRA IVANOVNA, *and walks up to her sister.*)

ALEXANDRA.

He is frightfully excited.   He has been to see Boris, and on returning he saw the dancing going on.   He wants to go away.   I went up to his door, and heard his conversation with Alexander Petrovich.

MARIE.

What did they say ?

VOICE FROM THE DANCE.

Rond des dames.   Les cavaliers en avant.

ALEXANDRA.

He has made up his mind that he cannot possibly continue to live here, and he is going away.

MARIE.

What a torment that man is!

(*Exit* MARIE IVANOVNA.)

SCENE II.

Nicholas Ivanovich's room. Music is heard from afar. NICHOLAS IVANOVICH *has his coat on, and puts a letter on the table. With him is a tramp,* ALEXANDER PETROVICH, *in rags.*

ALEXANDER.

Don't be uneasy. We can get to the Caucasus without a penny; and when we are once there you can arrange matters.

NICHOLAS.

We will take the train to Tula, and then we will go on foot. Now we're ready. (*Puts the letter in the middle of the table, and goes towards the door. Meets* MARIE IVANOVNA, *who enters.*)

NICHOLAS.

What have you come for?

MARIE.

To see what you are doing.

NICHOLAS.

I am suffering terribly.

MARIE.

What have I come for? Not to let you do a cruel thing. Why do you do it? What have I done?

NICHOLAS.

Why? Because I cannot go on living like this; I cannot endure this horrible life of depravity!

MARIE.

But this is awful. You call my life, which I devote to you and to the children, depraved! (*Noticing the presence of* ALEXANDER PETROVICH.) *Renvoyez au moins cet homme. Je ne veux pas qu'il soit témoin de cette conversation.*

ALEXANDER

(*in broken French*). *Comprenez toujours moi parté.*

NICHOLAS.

Wait for me outside, Alexander Petrovich. I will come directly.

(*Exit* ALEXANDER PETROVICH.)

MARIE.

What can you have in common with that man?
Why he is more to you than your wife passes all
comprehension.   Where do you intend to go?

NICHOLAS.

I was leaving a letter for you.   I did not want
to talk about it.   It is too painful.   But if you
wish I will try to tell you calmly what is in it.

MARIE.

No; I absolutely cannot understand why you
hate and punish the wife who has given up everything for you.   Can you say that I go out into
society, that I love dress or flirtations?   No! my
whole life has been devoted to my family.   I
nursed all my children myself; I brought them
up myself; and during these last years the whole
burden of their education and all the management
of our affairs has fallen on me.

NICHOLAS

(*interrupting*).   But all the weight of that burden
is due to your refusal to lead the life I proposed.

MARIE.

But what you proposed was impossible.   Ask
anybody!   I could not let the children grow up

illiterate, as you desired; and I could not do the cooking and the washing with my own hands.

NICHOLAS.

I never asked you to.

MARIE.

Well, something very like it. You call yourself a Christian, and you want to do good in the world. You say you love humanity. Then why do you torment the woman who has given her whole life to you?

NICHOLAS.

In what way am I tormenting you? I love you, but——

MARIE.

Is it not tormenting me to leave me and to go away? What will all the world say? One of the two—either that I am a bad, wicked woman, or that you are mad.

NICHOLAS.

Let them say I am mad then. I cannot live like this.

MARIE.

Why is it so terrible that I should give a party ?—the only one during the whole season, for fear of grieving you. I only did it because every one said it was a necessity.   Ask Mary, ask Varvara Vasilievna.   You treat this as a crime, and make me suffer disgrace for it.   It is not so much the disgrace I mind.   The worst of it is that you do not love me—you love the whole world, even that drunkard Alexander Petrovich. . . . But I still love you—I cannot live without you.   What have I done? what have I done?   (*She weeps.*)

NICHOLAS.

You will not understand my life—my spiritual life.

MARIE.

I do want to, but I can't.   I only see that your idea of Christianity makes you hate your family, and hate me.   Why, I do not understand.

NICHOLAS.

But others understand.

MARIE.

Who? Alexander Petrovich, who gets money from you?

NICHOLAS.

He and Ermilovich, Tonia, and Vasily.   But that is immaterial.   If no one understood, it would alter nothing.

MARIE.

Vasily Ermilovich has repented, and has returned to his parish; and at this very moment Tonia is dancing and flirting with Stephen.

NICHOLAS.

I am very sorry. But this cannot make black white, nor can it change my life. Masha, you do not need me—let me go! I have tried to take part in your life—to bring into it the thing that is life to me—but it cannot be done. The only result is that I torture both you and myself; and it is not only torture to me, but it ruins everything I attempt. Everybody — even that very Alexander Petrovich—has the right to say, and does say, that I am an impostor; that I say one thing and do another; that I preach the poverty of Christ and live in luxury, under cover of having given everything to my wife.

MARIE.

Then you are ashamed of yourself before the world? Are you not above that?

NICHOLAS.

It is not that I am ashamed of myself—though I certainly am—but that I am hindering the work of God.

MARIE.

You say yourself that the work of God goes on

in spite of all opposition. But leaving that aside, tell me what you want me to do.

NICHOLAS.

I have told you.

MARIE.

But, Nicholas, you know that that is impossible. Think of it. Luba is just going to be married, Vania has entered the university, and Missie and Katia are at school: how could I interrupt all that?

NICHOLAS.

But I? What am I to do?

MARIE.

Practise what you preach: endure and love. Is that so difficult? Only put up with us—do not deprive us of yourself! What is it that distresses you so?

(VANIA *rushes in.*)

VANIA.

Mother, you are wanted.

MARIE.

Say I can't come. Go; go away.

VANIA.

Please come!

(*Exit*).

NICHOLAS.

You will not see my point of view, and understand me.

MARIE.

I only wish I could.

NICHOLAS.

No, you do not wish to understand; and we are growing farther and farther apart. Put yourself in my place for a moment and think, and you will understand. In the first place, life here is depraved—such words anger you, but I can use no other when speaking of a life founded on robbery—because the money you live on comes from the land you have stolen from the people. Besides, I see how the children are being corrupted by it. "Woe to him who offends one of these little ones!"—and before my very eyes I see my children ruined and corrupted. Nor can I bear to see grown men dressed up in swallowtailed coats serving us as though they were slaves. Every meal is a misery.

MARIE.

But it has always been so. It is so in all houses —abroad and everywhere.

NICHOLAS.

Since I have realized that we are all brothers, I cannot look on without pain.

MARIE.

It is your own fault.   One can imagine anything.

NICHOLAS

(*hotly*).   This want of understanding is awful. To-day I spent the morning among the scavengers in the Rijánov Night Lodgings.   I saw a child dying of starvation, a boy that had become a drunkard, a consumptive laundress going to rinse her linen in the river, and I come home and a footman in a white tie opens my front door to me.   I hear my son, a young boy, tell that footman to bring him a glass of water, and I see a regiment of servants that work for us. Then I go to Boris, who is giving up his life for the truth, and I see this pure, strong, resolute man deliberately driven to madness and to death in order that they may get rid of him.   I know, and they know, that he has organic heart trouble ; and they provoke him, and then put him among raving maniacs !   Oh, it is awful !   And now I return home to learn that my daughter— the only one of my family who understood not me, but the truth—has thrown over both the truth and the man she was engaged to, and has promised to love, and is going to marry a flunkey—a liar.

MARIE.

What a very Christian sentiment!

NICHOLAS.

Yes, it is wrong. I am to blame. But I want you to enter into my feeling. I only say that she has repudiated the truth.

MARIE.

You say the truth. The rest, the majority, say error. Vasily Ermilovich thought he had gone astray, but now he has returned to the Church.

NICHOLAS.

It is impossible.

MARIE.

He wrote all about it to Lisa, and she will show you the letter. These things do not last. It's the same with Tonia, not to mention Alexander Petrovich, who simply finds it profitable.

NICHOLAS

(*getting angry*). That is immaterial. I only want you to understand me. I still consider that truth remains truth. It is painful to me to come home and see a Christmas tree, a ball, hundreds squandered when others are dying of hunger. I can *not* live like this! Have mercy on me! I am worn out. Let me go! Good-bye!

MARIE.

If you go, I go with you; and if not with you, I will throw myself under your train. Let them all perish—all—Missie—Katia—all of them. My God, my God, what anguish! Why is it?

(Sobbing.)

NICHOLAS

(*calling at the door*). Alexander Petrovich! Go. I shall not go with you. I shall stay. (*Takes off his coat.*)

MARIE.

We have not much longer to live. Do not let us spoil our life after twenty-eight years together. I will not give any more parties, but do not pain me so!

(VANIA *and* KATIA *rush in.*)

BOTH.

Mother, come quick!

MARIE.

I'm coming—I'm coming! Then let us forgive each other.

(*Exeunt* MARIE IVANOVNA *and* CHILDREN.)

NICHOLAS

(*alone*). A child—a perfect child! Or—a cunning woman! Ah, yes—a cunning child. That is it! O Thou dost not desire me for Thy servant. Thou wouldest humiliate me that all should point at me and say, "He talks but he does not act." I submit. He knows best what He desires. Humility, simplicity. Oh! if I could only raise myself to Him. (*Enter* LISA.)

LISA.

Excuse me : I came to bring you a letter from Vasily Ermilovich. It was written to me, but he wanted me to tell you about it.

NICHOLAS.

Is it really true then ?

LISA.

Yes. Read what he says.

NICHOLAS.

Will you read it to me ?

LISA

(*reading*). "I am writing to ask you to communicate this to Nicholas Ivanovich. I profoundly regret the error which made me openly renounce the Holy Orthodox Church, and I rejoice in my return.　I wish the same for you and for Nicholas Ivanovich, and I ask your forgiveness."

NICHOLAS.

They have driven the poor man to this, but still it is terrible.

LISA.

I wanted to tell you also that the Princess has come.　She came into my room in a terrible state of excitement, and says she must see you.　She has just come from Boris.　I think you had better not see her.　What good could it do?

NICHOLAS.

No, call her in.　Evidently this is to be a terrible day of trial.

LISA.

Then I'll call her.　(*Exit.*)

NICHOLAS

(*alone*).　Oh, just to remember that life consists in serving Thee!　To remember that if Thou sendest trials to me, it is that Thou thinkest that I am able to bear them; that they are not above my strength, otherwise it would not be a trial.　Father, help me—help me to do Thy will, and not my own.

(*Enter* PRINCESS.)

PRINCESS.

Oh, so you have admitted me—you have deigned to receive me. I will not shake your hand, because I hate and despise you.

NICHOLAS.

What has happened?

PRINCESS.

Just this! He is being transferred to the disciplinary battalion, and it is your doing.

NICHOLAS.

Princess, if you want anything, tell me what it is. If you have only come to abuse me, you are merely doing yourself harm. As for me, you cannot offend me, because I sympathize with you, and pity you with all my soul.

PRINCESS.

How charitable! Sublime Christianity! No, Monsieur Sarintsev, you cannot deceive me. I know you now. It is nothing to you that you have ruined my son, and here you are giving balls. Your daughter, who is engaged to my son, is about to make a match of which you approve, while you pretend to lead the simple life—you play at carpentering. How hateful you are to me, with your pharisaical life!

NICHOLAS.

Calm yourself, Princess, and tell me what you want. You have not come simply to abuse me.

PRINCESS.

Yes, partly. I had to pour out my anguish. What I want of you is this : they are sending him to the disciplinary battalion, and I cannot bear that. And it is you who have done it—you— you—you !

NICHOLAS.

Not I—God has done it. And God knows how I pity you. Do not set yourself in opposition to the will of God. He is testing you. Bear it humbly.

PRINCESS.

I cannot bear it humbly. My son is all the world to me, and you have taken him from me and have ruined him. I cannot accept it quietly. I have come to you, and I tell you again, and for the last time, that you have brought about his ruin, and you must save him. Go and obtain his release—go to the authorities, to the Tsar, to whomever you will. It is your duty. If you will not, I know what I shall do. You will answer to me for what you have done.

NICHOLAS.

Tell me what I am to do. I am willing to do all I can.

PRINCESS.

I repeat once more, you must save him. If you do not—remember. Good-bye. (*Exit.*)

> (NICHOLAS *lies down on the sofa. Silence. Pause. Music of "Grossvater's Tanz" is distinctly heard.*)

STEPHEN.

Father isn't here. Come on.

> (*Enter chain of dancers, adults and children.*)

LUBA

(*seeing her father*). Oh, you are here! I beg your pardon!

NICHOLAS

(*rising*). Never mind. (*Chain goes through the room and out at the other door.*) (*Alone.*) Vasily Ermilovich has returned to the Church. Boris is ruined through me. Luba will marry. Is it possible that I am mistaken — mistaken in believing Thee? Ah no! Father, help me!

ACT V.

Scene I.

A cell in the disciplinary battalion. Prisoners *sitting or lying about.* Boris *reading the Gospel and making comments.*

A man who has been flogged led out from this cell: "Oh, why is there not another Pugachev to avenge us?"

Princess *rushes in. She is turned out. Struggle with an* Officer.

Prisoners *ordered to prayers.*

Boris *sent to the dungeon, and sentenced to be flogged.*

Scene II.

The Tsar's study. Cigarettes. Jokes. Blandishments.

Princess *is announced. Ordered to wait.*
Cringing Petitioners.
Then enter Princess. *Request refused. Exeunt.*

Scene III.

Marie Ivanovna

(*speaks with* Doctor *of illness of* Nicholas Ivanovich). He has changed, is very mild, but dejected.

Nicholas Ivanovich

(*enters with* Doctor). Treatment is futile. The soul is more important, but I consent for the sake of my wife.

Enter Tonia *with* Stephen, Luba *with* Starkovsky. *Talk of the land.* Nicholas Ivanovich *tries not to offend the others.* *All go.*

Nicholas

(*alone with* Lisa). I am in a state of continual vacillation. Have I done right? I have achieved nothing. I have ruined Boris. Vasily Ermilovich has returned to the Church. I am an example of weakness. I see God did not want me to be His servant. He has many other servants. They will do the right thing without me. To see that clearly is to obtain peace of mind.

(Lisa *goes. He prays.*)

Princess *dashes in and kills him.* *All rush in.* *He says he did it himself accidentally.* *Writes petition to the Tsar.*

Enter VASILY ERMILOVICH *with* DUKHOBORS. NICHOLAS IVANOVICH *dies rejoicing that the falsehoods of the Church are broken down. He realizes the meaning of his life.*

ALTERNATIVE FOR LAST SCENE.

Letter from BORIS *full of desperate agitation :* "I know—I have also passed through that."

LIBERALS.—*A professor from the height of his superiority forgives and explains.*

A Liberal society lady, wearing diamonds, present : "They are unable to understand. It will take a hundred years for them to do so."

THERE ARE NO GUILTY PEOPLE.

THERE ARE NO GUILTY PEOPLE.

I.

MINE is a strange and wonderful lot! The chances are that there is not a single wretched beggar suffering under the luxury and oppression of the rich who feels anything like as keenly as I do either the injustice, the cruelty, and the horror of their oppression of and contempt for the poor; or the grinding humiliation and misery which befall the great majority of the workers, the real producers of all that makes life possible. I have felt this for a long time, and as the years have passed by the feeling has grown and grown, until recently it reached its climax. Although I feel all this so vividly, I still live on amid the depravity and sins of rich society; and I cannot leave it, because I have neither the knowledge nor the strength to do so. I cannot. I do not know how to change my life so that my physical needs —food, sleep, clothing, my going to and fro—

may be satisfied without a sense of shame and wrongdoing in the position which I fill.

There was a time when I tried to change my position, which was not in harmony with my conscience ; but the conditions created by the past, by my family and its claims upon me, were so complicated that they would not let me out of their grasp, or, rather, I did not know how to free myself. I had not the strength. Now that I am over eighty and have become feeble, I have given up trying to free myself ; and, strange to say, as my feebleness increases I realize more and more strongly the wrongfulness of my position, and it grows more and more intolerable to me.

It has occurred to me that I do not occupy this position for nothing : that Providence intended that I should lay bare the truth of my feelings, so that I might atone for all that causes my suffering, and might perhaps open the eyes of those—or at least of some of those—who are still blind to what I see so clearly, and thus might lighten the burden of that vast majority who, under existing conditions, are subjected to bodily and spiritual suffering by those who deceive them and also deceive themselves. Indeed, it may be that the position which I occupy gives me special facilities for revealing the artificial and criminal relations which exist between men—for telling the whole truth in regard to that position without confusing the issue by attempting to vindicate myself, and without rousing the envy of the rich and feelings of oppression in the hearts of the poor and down-trodden. I am so placed that I not only have no desire to vindicate myself ; but, on the contrary, I find it necessary to make an effort lest I should exaggerate the wickedness of the great among whom I live, of whose society I am ashamed, whose attitude towards their fellow-men I detest with my whole soul, though I find it impossible to separate my lot from theirs. But I must also avoid the error of those democrats and others who, in defending the oppressed and the enslaved, do not see their failings and mistakes, and who do not make sufficient allowance for the difficulties created, the mistakes inherited from the past, which in a degree lessens the responsibility of the upper classes.

Free from desire for self-vindication, free from fear of an emancipated people, free from that envy and hatred which the oppressed feel for their oppressors, I am in the best possible position to see the truth and to tell it. Perhaps that is why Providence placed me in such a position. I will do my best to turn it to account.

10

II.

Alexander Ivanovich Volgin, a bachelor and a clerk in a Moscow bank at a salary of eight thousand roubles a year, a man much respected in his own set, was staying in a country-house. His host was a wealthy landowner, owning some twenty-five hundred acres, and had married his guest's cousin. Volgin, tired after an evening spent in playing vint * for small stakes with members of the family, went to his room and placed his watch, silver cigarette-case, pocket-book, big leather purse, and pocket brush and comb on a small table covered with a white cloth, and then, taking off his coat, waistcoat, shirt, trousers, and underclothes, his silk socks and English boots, put on his nightshirt and dressing-gown. His watch pointed to midnight. Volgin smoked a cigarette, lay on his face for about five minutes reviewing the day's impressions ; then, blowing out his candle, he turned over on his side and fell asleep about one o'clock, in spite of a good deal of restlessness. Awaking next morning at eight he put on his slippers and dressing-gown, and rang the bell. The old butler, Stephen, the father of a family and the grandfather of six grandchildren,

* A game of cards similar to auction bridge.

who had served in that house for thirty years, entered the room hurriedly, with bent legs, carrying in the newly blackened boots which Volgin had taken off the night before, a well-brushed suit, and a clean shirt. The guest thanked him, and then asked what the weather was like (the blinds were drawn so that the sun should not prevent any one from sleeping till eleven o'clock if he were so inclined), and whether his host had slept well. He glanced at his watch—it was still early—and began to wash and dress. His water was ready, and everything on the washing-stand and dressing-table was ready for use and properly laid out—his soap, his tooth and hair brushes, his nail scissors and files. He washed his hands and face in a leisurely fashion, cleaned and manicured his nails, pushed back the skin with the towel, and sponged his stout white body from head to foot. Then he began to brush his hair. Standing in front of the mirror, he first brushed his curly beard, which was beginning to turn grey, with two English brushes, parting it down the middle. Then he combed his hair, which was already showing signs of getting thin, with a large tortoise-shell comb. Putting on his underlinen, his socks, his boots, his trousers —which were held up by elegant braces—and his waistcoat, he sat down coatless in an easy chair to rest after dressing, lit a cigarette, and began to

think where he should go for a walk that morning
—to the park or to Littleports (what a funny
name for a wood!). He thought he would go
to Littleports. Then he must answer Simon
Nicholaevich's letter; but there was time enough
for that. Getting up with an air of resolution, he
took out his watch. It was already five minutes
to nine. He put his watch into his waistcoat
pocket, and his purse—with all that was left of
the hundred and eighty roubles he had taken for his
journey, and for the incidental expenses of his fortnight's stay with his cousin—and then he placed into
his trouser pocket his cigarette-case and electric
cigarette-lighter, and two clean handkerchiefs into
his coat pockets, and went out of the room, leaving as
usual the mess and confusion which he had made
to be cleared up by Stephen, an old man of over
fifty. Stephen expected Volgin to "remunerate"
him, as he said, being so accustomed to the work
that he did not feel the slightest repugnance for it.
Glancing at a mirror, and feeling satisfied with his
appearance, Volgin went into the dining-room.

There, thanks to the efforts of the housekeeper,
the footman, and under-butler — the latter had
risen at dawn in order to run home to sharpen his
son's scythe—breakfast was ready. On a spotless
white cloth stood a boiling, shiny, silver samovar
(at least it looked like silver), a coffee-pot, hot

milk, cream, butter, and all sorts of fancy white bread and biscuits. The only persons at table were the second son of the house, his tutor (a student), and the secretary. The host, who was an active member of the Zemstvo and a great farmer, had already left the house, having gone at eight o'clock to attend to his work. Volgin, while drinking his coffee, talked to the student and the secretary about the weather, and yesterday's vint, and discussed Theodorite's peculiar behaviour the night before, as he had been very rude to his father without the slightest cause. Theodorite was the grown-up son of the house, and a ne'er-do-well. His name was Theodore, but some one had once called him Theodorite either as a joke or to tease him ; and, as it seemed funny, the name stuck to him, although his doings were no longer in the least amusing. So it was now. He had been to the university, but left it in his second year, and joined a regiment of horse guards ; but he gave that up also, and was now living in the country, doing nothing, finding fault, and feeling discontented with everything. Theodorite was still in bed : so were the other members of the household—Anna Mikhailovna, its mistress ; her sister, the widow of a general ; and a landscape painter who lived with the family.

Volgin took his panama hat from the hall table

(it had cost twenty roubles) and his cane with its carved ivory handle, and went out. Crossing the veranda, gay with flowers, he walked through the flower garden, in the centre of which was a raised round bed, with rings of red, white, and blue flowers, and the initials of the mistress of the house done in carpet bedding in the centre. Leaving the flower garden Volgin entered the avenue of lime trees, hundreds of years old, which peasant girls were tidying and sweeping with spades and brooms. The gardener was busy measuring, and a boy was bringing something in a cart. Passing these Volgin went into the park of at least a hundred and twenty-five acres, filled with fine old trees, and intersected by a network of well-kept walks. Smoking as he strolled Volgin took his favourite path past the summer-house into the fields beyond. It was pleasant in the park, but it was still nicer in the fields. On the right some women who were digging potatoes formed a mass of bright red and white colour ; on the left were wheat fields, meadows, and grazing cattle ; and in the foreground, slightly to the right, were the dark, dark oaks of Littleports. Volgin took a deep breath, and felt glad that he was alive, especially here in his cousin's home, where he was so thoroughly enjoying the rest from his work at the bank.

"Lucky people to live in the country," he thought. "True, what with his farming and his Zemstvo, the owner of the estate has very little peace even in the country, but that is his own lookout." Volgin shook his head, lit another cigarette, and, stepping out firmly with his powerful feet clad in his thick English boots, began to think of the heavy winter's work in the bank that was in front of him. "I shall be there every day from ten to two, sometimes even till five. And the board meetings . . . And private interviews with clients . . . Then the Duma. Whereas here . . . It is delightful. It may be a little dull, but it is not for long." He smiled. After a stroll in Littleports he turned back, going straight across a fallow field which was being ploughed. A herd of cows, calves, sheep, and pigs, which belonged to the village community, was grazing there. The shortest way to the park was to pass through the herd. He frightened the sheep, which ran away one after another, and were followed by the pigs, of which two little ones stared solemnly at him. The shepherd boy called to the sheep and cracked his whip. "How far behind Europe we are," thought Volgin, recalling his frequent holidays abroad. "You would not find a single cow like that anywhere in Europe." Then, wanting to find out where the path which

branched off from the one he was on led to and
who was the owner of the herd, he called to the
boy—

"Whose herd is it?"

The boy was so filled with wonder, verging on
terror, when he gazed at the hat, the well-brushed
beard, and above all the gold-rimmed eyeglasses,
that he could not reply at once. When Volgin
repeated his question the boy pulled himself
together, and said, "Ours."

"But whose is 'ours?'" said Volgin, shaking
his head and smiling. The boy was wearing
shoes of plaited birch bark, bands of linen round
his legs, a dirty, unbleached shirt ragged at the
shoulder, and a cap the peak of which had been
torn. "Whose is 'ours'?"

"The Pirogov village herd."

"How old are you?"

"I don't know."

"Can you read?"

"No, I can't."

"Didn't you go to school?"

"Yes, I did."

"Couldn't you learn to read?"

"No."

"Where does that path lead?"

The boy told him, and Volgin went on towards
the house, thinking how he would chaff Nicholas

Petrovich about the deplorable condition of the village schools in spite of all his efforts.

On approaching the house Volgin looked at his watch, and saw that it was already past eleven. He remembered that Nicholas Petrovich was going to drive to the nearest town, and that he had meant to give him a letter to post to Moscow ; but the letter was not written. The letter was a very important one to a friend, asking him to bid for him for a picture of the Madonna which was to be offered for sale at an auction. As he reached the house he saw at the door four big, well-fed, well-groomed, thorough-bred horses harnessed to a carriage, the black lacquer of which glistened in the sun. The coachman was seated on the box in a kaftan, with a silver belt, and the horses were jingling their silver bells from time to time. A bare-headed, bare-footed peasant in a ragged kaftan stood at the front door. He bowed. Volgin asked what he wanted.

" I have come to see Nicholas Petrovich.

" What about ? "

" Because I am in distress—my horse has died."

Volgin began to question him. The peasant told him how he was situated. He had five children, and this had been his only horse. Now it was gone. He wept.

" What are you going to do ? "

10 a

"To beg." And he knelt down, and remained kneeling in spite of Volgin's expostulations.

"What is your name?"

"Mitri Sudarikov," answered the peasant, still kneeling.

Volgin took three roubles from his purse and gave them to the peasant, who showed his gratitude by touching the ground with his forehead, and then went into the house. His host was standing in the hall.

"Where is your letter?" he asked, approaching Volgin; "I am just off."

"I'm awfully sorry, I'll write it this minute, if you will let me. I forgot all about it. It's so pleasant here that one can forget anything."

"All right, but do be quick. The horses have already been standing a quarter of an hour, and the flies are biting viciously. Can you wait, Arsenty?" he asked the coachman.

"Why not?" said the coachman, thinking to himself, "Why do they order the horses when they aren't ready? The rush the grooms and I had—just to stand here and feed the flies."

"Directly, directly." Volgin went towards his room, but turned back to ask Nicholas Petrovich about the begging peasant.

"Did you see him?—He's a drunkard, but still he is to be pitied. Do be quick!"

Volgin got out his case, with all the requisites

for writing, wrote the letter, made out a cheque for a hundred and eighty roubles, and, sealing down the envelope, took it to Nicholas Petrovich.

"Good-bye."

Volgin read the newspapers till luncheon. He only read the Liberal papers : *The Russian Gazette*, *Speech*, sometimes *The Russian Word*—but he would not touch *The New Times*, to which his host subscribed.

While he was scanning at his ease the political news—the Tsar's doings, the doings of President and ministers and decisions in the Duma—and was just about to pass on to the general news— theatres, science, murders, and cholera—he heard the luncheon bell ring.

Thanks to the efforts of upwards of ten human beings—counting laundresses, gardeners, cooks, kitchen-maids, butler, and footmen—the table was sumptuously laid for eight, with silver water-jugs, decanters, kvass, wine, mineral waters, cut glass, and fine table linen, while two men-servants were continually hurrying to and fro, bringing in and serving, and then clearing away the *hors-d'œuvre* and the various hot and cold courses.

The hostess talked incessantly about everything that she had been doing, thinking, and saying ; and she evidently considered that everything that she thought, said, or did was perfect, and that it would

please every one except those who were fools.
Volgin felt and knew that everything she said was
stupid, but it would never do to let it be seen, and so
he kept up the conversation. Theodorite was glum
and silent ; the student occasionally exchanged a few
words with the widow. Now and again there was a
pause in the conversation, and then Theodorite inter-
posed, and every one became miserably depressed.
At such moments the hostess ordered some dish
that had not been served, and the footman hurried
off to the kitchen, or to the housekeeper, and
hurried back again. Nobody felt inclined either
to talk or to eat. But they all forced themselves
to eat and to talk, and so luncheon went on.

The peasant who had been begging because his
horse had died was named Mitri Sudarikov. He
had spent the whole day before he went to the
squire over his dead horse. First of all he went
to the knacker, Sanin, who lived in a village near.
The knacker was out, but he waited for him, and
it was dinner-time when he had finished bargaining
over the price of the skin. Then he borrowed a
neighbour's horse to take his own to a field to be
buried, as it is forbidden to bury dead animals near
a village. Adrian would not lend his horse because
he was getting in his potatoes, but Stephen took
pity on Mitri and gave way to his persuasion.
He even lent a hand in lifting the dead horse

into the cart. Mitri tore off the shoes from the forelegs and gave them to his wife. One was broken, but the other one was whole. While he was digging the grave with a spade which was very blunt, the knacker appeared and took off the skin; and the carcass was then thrown into the hole and covered up. Mitri felt tired, and went into Matrena's hut, where he drank half a bottle of vodka with Sanin to console himself. Then he went home, quarrelled with his wife, and lay down to sleep on the hay. He did not undress, but slept just as he was, with a ragged coat for a coverlet. His wife was in the hut with the girls— there were four of them, and the youngest was only five weeks old. Mitri woke up before dawn as usual. He groaned as the memory of the day before broke in upon him—how the horse had struggled and struggled, and then fallen down. Now there was no horse, and all he had was the price of the skin, four roubles and eighty kopeks. Getting up he arranged the linen bands on his legs, and went through the yard into the hut. His wife was putting straw into the stove with one hand, with the other she was holding a baby girl to her breast, which was hanging out of her dirty chemise.

Mitri crossed himself three times, turning towards the corner in which the ikons hung, and repeated some utterly meaningless words, which he called prayers, to the Trinity and the Virgin, the Creed and our Father.

"Isn't there any water?"

"The girl's gone for it. I've got some tea. Will you go up to the squire?"

"Yes, I'd better." The smoke from the stove made him cough. He took a rag off the wooden bench and went into the porch. The girl had just come back with the water. Mitri filled his mouth with water from the pail and squirted it out on his hands, took some more in his mouth to wash his face, dried himself with the rag, then parted and smoothed his curly hair with his fingers and went out. A little girl of about ten, with nothing on but a dirty shirt, came towards him. "Good-morning, Uncle Mitri," she said; "you are to come and thrash."

"All right, I'll come," replied Mitri. He understood that he was expected to return the help given the week before by Kumushkir, a man as poor as he was himself, when he was thrashing his own corn with a horse-driven machine. "Tell them I'll come—I'll come at lunch time. I've got to go to Ugrumi."

Mitri went back to the hut, and changing his birch-bark shoes and the linen bands on his legs, started off to see the squire. After he had got three roubles from Volgin, and the same sum from Nicholas Petrovich, he returned to his house, gave the money to his wife, and went to his neighbour's. The thrashing-machine was humming, and the driver was shouting. The lean horses were going slowly round him, straining at their traces. The driver was shouting to them in a monotone, "Now there, my dears." Some women were unbinding sheaves, others were raking up the scattered straw and ears, and others again were gathering great armfuls of corn and handing them to the men to feed the machine. The work was in full swing. In the kitchen garden, which Mitri had to pass, a girl, clad only in a long shirt, was digging potatoes which she put into a basket.

"Where's your grandfather?" asked Mitri.

"He's in the barn."

Mitri went to the barn and set to work at once. The old man of eighty knew of Mitri's trouble. After greeting him, he gave him his place to feed the machine.

Mitri took off his ragged coat, laid it out of the way near the fence, and then began to work vigorously, raking the corn together and throwing it into the machine. The work went on without interruption until the dinner-hour. The cocks had crowed two or three times, but no one paid any attention to them ; not because the workers did not believe them, but because they were scarcely heard for the noise of the work and the talk about it. At last the whistle of the squire's steam thrasher sounded three miles away, and then the owner came into the barn. He was a straight old man of eighty.

"It's time to stop," he said; "it's dinner-time."

Those at work seemed to redouble their efforts. In a moment the straw was cleared away ; the grain that had been thrashed was separated from the chaff and brought in, and then the workers went into the hut.

The hut was smoke begrimed, as its stove had no chimney, but it had been tidied up, and benches stood round the table, making room for all those who had been working, of whom there were nine, not counting the owners. Bread, soup, boiled potatoes, and kvass were placed on the table.

An old one-armed beggar, with a bag slung over his shoulder, came in with a crutch during the meal.

"Peace be to this house. A good appetite to you. For Christ's sake, give me something."

"God will give to you," said the mistress, already an old woman, and the daughter-in-law of the master. "Don't be angry with us."

An old man, who was still standing near the door, said—

" Give him some bread, Martha. How can you ?"

" I am only wondering whether we shall have enough."

" Oh, it is wrong, Martha. God tells us to help the poor. Cut him a slice."

Martha obeyed. The beggar went away. The man in charge of the thrashing-machine got up, said grace, thanked his hosts, and went away to rest.

Mitri did not lie down, but ran to the shop to buy some tobacco. He was longing for a smoke. While he smoked he chatted to a man from Demensk, asking the price of cattle, as he saw that he would not be able to manage without selling a cow. When he returned to the others, they were already back at work again ; and so it went on till the evening.

Among these downtrodden, duped, and de-frauded men, who are becoming demoralized by overwork and being gradually done to death by underfeeding, there are men living who consider themselves Christians ; and others so enlightened that they feel no further need for Christianity or for any religion, so superior do they appear in their own esteem. And yet their hideous, lazy lives are supported by the degrading, excessive labour of these slaves, not to mention the labour of millions of other slaves, toiling in factories to produce samovars, silver, carriages, machines, and the like for their use. They live among these horrors, seeing them and yet not seeing them, although often kind at heart—old men and women, young men and maidens, mothers and children—poor children who are being vitiated and trained into moral blindness.

Here is a bachelor grown old, the owner of thousands of acres, who has lived a life of idleness, greed, and over-indulgence, who reads *The New Times*, and is astonished that the government can be so unwise as to permit Jews to enter the university. There is his guest, formerly the governor of a province, now a senator with a big salary, who reads with satisfaction that a congress of lawyers has passed a resolution in favour of capital punishment. Their political enemy, N.P., reads a Liberal paper, and cannot understand the blindness of the government in allowing the union of Russian men to exist.

Here is a kind, gentle mother of a little girl reading a story to her about Fox, a dog that lamed some rabbits. And here is this little girl. During her walks she sees other children, bare-footed, hungry, hunting for green apples that have fallen from the trees ; and, so accustomed is she to the sight, that these children do not seem to her to be children such as she is, but only part of the usual surroundings—the familiar landscape.

Why is this ?

THE WISDOM OF CHILDREN.

THE WISDOM OF CHILDREN

ON RELIGION.

Boy.

WHY is Nurse so nicely dressed to-day, and why did she make me wear that new shirt?

MOTHER.

Because this is a holiday, and we are going to church.

Boy.

What holiday?

MOTHER.

Ascension Day.

Boy.

What does Ascension mean?

MOTHER.

It means that Jesus Christ has ascended to heaven.

Boy.

What does that mean—ascended?

MOTHER.

It means that He flew up to heaven.

Boy.

How did He fly ?—with His wings ?

Mother.

Without any wings whatever. He simply flew up because He is God, and God can do anything.

Boy.

But where did He fly to ? Father told me there was nothing in heaven at all, and we only think we see something ; that there's nothing but stars up there, and behind them more stars still, and that there is no end to it. Then where did He fly to ?

Mother

(*smiling*). You are unable to understand everything. You must believe.

Boy.

What must I believe ?

Mother.

What you are told by grown-up people.

Boy.

But when I said to you that somebody was going to die because some salt had been spilt, you said I was not to believe in nonsense.

MOTHER.

Of course you are not to believe in nonsense.

BOY.

But how am I to know what is nonsense and what is not?

MOTHER.

You must believe what the true faith says, and not in nonsense.

BOY.

Which is the true faith then?

MOTHER.

Our faith is the true one. (*To herself*) I am afraid I am talking nonsense. (*Aloud*) Go and tell father we are ready for church, and get your coat.

BOY.

And shall we have chocolate after church?

ON WAR.

KARLCHEN SCHMIDT, *nine years*; PETIA ORLOV, *ten years; and* MASHA ORLOV, *eight years.*

KARLCHEN.

. . . Because we Prussians will not allow Russia to rob us of our land.

PETIA.

But we say this land belongs to us; we conquered it first.

MASHA.

To whom? Is it ours?

PETIA.

You are a child, and you don't understand. "To us" means to our state.

KARLCHEN.

It is this way : some belong to one state and some to another.

MASHA.

What do I belong to?

PETIA.

You belong to Russia, like the rest of us.

MASHA.

And if I don't want to ?

PETIA.

It doesn't matter whether you want to or not. You are Russian, all the same. Every nation has its Tsar, its King.

KARLCHEN

(*interrupting*). And a parliament.

PETIA.

Each state has its army ; each state raises taxes.

MASHA.

But why must each state stand by itself ?

PETIA.

What a silly question ! Because each state *is* a separate one.

MASHA.

But why must it exist apart ?

PETIA.

Can't you understand ? Because everybody loves his own country.

MASHA.

I don't understand why they must be separate from the rest. Wouldn't it be better if they all kept together ?

PETIA.

To keep together is all right when you play games. But this is no game ; it is a very serious matter.

MASHA.

I don't understand.

KARLCHEN.

You will when you grow up.

MASHA.

Then I don't want to grow up.

PETIA.

Such a tiny girl, and obstinate already, just like all of them.

ON STATE AND FATHERLAND.

GAVRILA, *a soldier in the reserve, a servant.*
MISHA, *his master's young son.*

GAVRILA.

Good-bye, Mishenka, my dear little master. Who knows whether God will permit me to see you again?

MISHA.

Are you really leaving?

GAVRILA.

I have to. There is war again; and I am in the reserve.

MISHA.

A war with whom? Who's fighting, and who are they fighting against?

GAVRILA.

God knows. It's very difficult to understand all that. I have read about it in the papers, but I can't make it out. They say that some one in Austria has a grudge against us because of some favour he did to what's-their-names . . .

MISHA.

But what are you fighting for ?

GAVRILA.

I am fighting for the Tsar, of course ; for my country and the Orthodox Faith.

MISHA.

But you don't wish to go to the war, do you ?

GAVRILA.

Certainly not. To leave my wife and my children . . . Do you suppose I would leave this happy life of my own free will ?

MISHA.

Then why do you go ? Tell them you don't want to, and stop here. What can they do to you ?

GAVRILA

(*laughing*). What can they do ? They will take me by force.

MISHA.

Who can take you by force ?

GAVRILA.

Men who have to obey, and who are exactly in my position.

MISHA.

Why will they take you by force if they are in the same position?

GAVRILA.

Because of the authorities. They will be ordered to take me, and they will have to do it.

MISHA.

But suppose they don't want to?

GAVRILA.

They have to obey.

MISHA.

But why?

GAVRILA.

Why? Because of the law.

MISHA.

What law?

GAVRILA.

You are a funny boy. It's a pleasure to chat with you. But now I had better go and get the samovar ready. It will be for the last time.

ON TAXES.

The BAILIFF and GRUSHKA.

BAILIFF

(*entering a poor cottage.   Nobody is in except* GRUSHKA, *a little girl of seven.   He looks around him*).   Nobody at home ?

GRUSHKA.

Mother has gone to bring home the cow, and Fedka is at work in the master's yard.

BAILIFF.

Well, tell your mother the bailiff called.   Tell her I am giving her notice for the third time, and that she must pay her taxes before Sunday without fail, or else I will take her cow.

GRUSHKA.

The cow ?   Are you a thief ?   We will not let you take our cow.

BAILIFF

(*smiling*).   What a smart girl, I say !   What is your name ?

GRUSHKA.

Grushka.

BAILIFF.

You are a good girl, Grushka. Now listen. Tell your mother that, although I am not a thief, I will take her cow.

GRUSHKA.

Why will you take our cow if you are not a thief?

BAILIFF.

Because what is due must be paid. I shall take the cow for the taxes that are not paid.

GRUSHKA.

What's that—taxes?

BAILIFF.

What a nuisance of a girl! What are taxes? They are money paid by the people by order of the Tsar.

GRUSHKA.

To whom?

BAILIFF.

The Tsar will look after that when the money comes in.

GRUSHKA.

He's not poor, is he? We are the poor people.

11

The Tsar is rich. Why does he want us to give him money?

BAILIFF.

He does not take it for himself; he spends it on us, fools that we are. It all goes to supply our needs — to pay the authorities, the army, the schools. It is for our own good that we pay taxes.

GRUSHKA.

How does it benefit us if our cow is taken away? There's no good in that.

BAILIFF.

You will understand that when you are grown up. Now, mind you give your mother my message.

GRUSHKA.

I will not repeat all your nonsense to her. You can do whatever you and the Tsar want, and we shall mind our own business.

BAILIFF.

What a devil of a girl she will be when she grows up!

ON JUDGING.

MITIA, *a boy of ten ;* ILIUSHA, *a boy of nine ;*
SONIA, *a girl of six.*

MITIA.

I told Peter Semenovich we could get used to
wearing no clothes at all. And he said, "That is
impossible." Then I told him Michael Ivanovich
said that just as we have managed to get our bare
faces used to the cold, we could do the same with
our whole body. Peter Semenovich said, "Your
Michael Ivanovich is a fool." (*He laughs.*) And
Michael Ivanovich said to me only yesterday,
"Peter Semenovich is talking a lot of nonsense.
But, of course," he added, "there's no law for
fools." (*He laughs.*)

ILIUSHA.

If I were you I would tell Peter Semenovich,
"You abuse Michael Ivanovich, and he does the
same to you."

MITIA.

No ; but truly, I wish I knew which of them is
the fool.

SONIA.

They both are. Whoever calls another person a fool is a fool himself.

ILIUSHA.

And you have called them both fools. Then you are one also.

MITIA.

Well, I hate people saying things about each other behind their backs and never openly to their faces. When I am grown-up I shan't be like that. I shall always say what I think.

ILIUSHA.

So shall I.

SONIA.

And I shall do just whatever I like.

MITIA.

What do you mean?

SONIA.

Why, I shall say what I think—if I choose. And if I don't choose, I won't.

ILIUSHA.

You're a big fool, that is what you are.

SONIA.

And you have just said you will never call people names. But of course . . .

ON KINDNESS.

The children, MASHA *and* MISHA, *are building a tent for their dolls in front of the house.*

MISHA

(*in an angry tone to* MASHA). No, not this. Bring that stick there. What a blockhead you are!

AN OLD WOMAN

(*coming out of the house, crossing herself, and muttering*). Jesus Christ reward her! What an angel! She has pity on every one.

> (*The* CHILDREN *cease to play, and look at the old woman.*)

MISHA.

Who is as good as all that?

OLD WOMAN.

Your mother. She has God in her soul. She pities us, the poor. She has given me a skirt— and some tea, and money too. The Queen of

Heaven save her! Not like that godless man. "Such a lot of you," he says, "tramping about here." And such savage dogs he has !

MISHA.

Who is that ?

OLD WOMAN.

The man opposite—the wine merchant. A very unkind gentleman, I can tell you. But never mind. I am so thankful to the dear lady. She has given me presents, has relieved me, miserable creature that I am. How could we exist if it were not for such kind people ? (*She weeps.*)

MASHA

(*to* MISHA). How good she is !

OLD WOMAN.

When you are grown up, children, be as kind as she is to the poor. God will reward you.

(*Exit.*)

MISHA.

How wretched she is !

MASHA.

I am so glad mother has given her something.

MISHA.

Why shouldn't one give, if one has got plenty

of everything oneself ? We are not poor, and
she is.

MASHA.

You remember John the Baptist said : Whoever
has two coats, let him give away one.

MISHA.

Oh, when I am grown up I will give away everything I have.

MASHA.

Not everything, I should think.

MISHA.

Why not ?

MASHA.

But what would you have left for yourself ?

MISHA.

I don't care. We must always be kind. Then
the whole world will be happy.

> (MISHA *stopped playing with his
> sister, went to the nursery, tore a page
> out of a copy-book, wrote a line on it,
> and put it in his pocket. On that page
> was written :* WE MUST BE KIND.)

ON REMUNERATION OF LABOUR.

The FATHER ; KATIA, *a girl of nine ;* FEDIA, *a boy of eight.*

KATIA.

Father, our sledge is broken. Couldn't you mend it for us ?

FATHER.

No, darling, I cannot. I don't know how to do it. Give it to Prohor ; he will put it right for you.

KATIA.

We have asked him to already. He says he is busy. He is making a gate.

FATHER.

Well, then, you must just wait a little with your sledge.

FEDIA.

And you, father, can't you mend it for us, really ?

FATHER

(*smiling*).   Really, my boy.

FEDIA.

Can't you do any work at all ?

FATHER

(*laughing*).   Oh yes, there are some kinds of work I can do, but not the kind that Prohor does.

FEDIA.

Can you make samovars like Vania ?

FATHER.

No.

FEDIA.

Or harness horses ?

FATHER.

Not that either.

FEDIA.

I wonder why are we all unable to do any work, and they do it all for us.   Ought it to be like that ?

FATHER.

Everybody has to do the work he is fit for. Learn, like a good boy, and you will know what work everybody has to do.

11 *a*

FEDIA.

Are we not to learn how to prepare food and to harness horses ?

FATHER.

There are things more necessary than that.

FEDIA.

I know : to be kind, not to get cross, not to abuse people. But isn't it possible to do the cooking and harness horses, and be kind just the same ? Isn't that possible ?

FATHER.

Undoubtedly. Just wait till you are grown up. Then you will understand.

FEDIA.

And what if I don't grow up ?

FATHER.

Don't talk nonsense !

KATIA.

Then we may ask Prohor to mend the sledge ?

FATHER.

Yes, do. Go to Prohor and tell him I wish him to do it.

ON DRINK.

An evening in the autumn.

(MAKARKA, *a boy of twelve, and*
MARFUTKA, *a girl of eight, are coming
out of the house into the street.* MAR-
FUTKA *is crying.* PAVLUSHKA, *a boy
of ten, stands before the house next door.*)

PAVLUSHKA.

Where the devil are you going to, both of you?
Have you any night work?

MAKARKA.

Crazy drunk again.

PAVLUSHKA.

Who? Uncle Prohor?

MAKARKA.

Of course.

MARFUTKA.

He is beating mother——

MAKARKA.

I won't go inside to-night. He would hit me also. (*Sitting down on the doorstep.*) I will stay here the whole night. I will.

(MARFUTKA *weeps.*)

PAVLUSHKA.

Stop crying. Never mind. It can't be helped. Stop crying, I say.

MARFUTKA.

If I was the Tsar, I would have the people who give him any drink just beaten to death. I would not allow anybody to sell brandy.

PAVLUSHKA.

Wouldn't you? But it is the Tsar himself who sells it. He doesn't let anybody else sell it, for fear it would lessen his own profits.

MARFUTKA.

It is a lie!

PAVLUSHKA.

Humph—a lie! You just ask anybody you like. Why have they put Akulina in prison? Because they did not want her to sell brandy and lessen their profits.

MAKARKA.

Is that really so? I heard she had done something against the law.

PAVLUSHKA.

What she did against the law was selling brandy.

MARFUTKA.

I would not allow her to sell it either. It is just that brandy that does all the mischief. Sometimes he is very nice, and then at other times he hits everybody.

MAKARKA

(*to* PAVLUSHKA). You say very strange things. I will ask the schoolmaster to-morrow; he must know.

PAVLUSHKA.

Do ask him.

> (*The next morning* PROHOR, MAKARKA'S *father, after a night's sleep, goes to refresh himself with a drink;* MAKARKA'S *mother, with a swollen eye, is kneading bread.* MAKARKA *has gone to school. The* SCHOOLMASTER *is sitting at the door of the village school, watching the children coming in.*)

MAKARKA

(*coming up to the schoolmaster*). Tell me, please, Eugene Semenovich, is it true, what a fellow was telling me, that the Tsar makes a business of sell-

ing brandy, and that is why Akulina has been sent
to prison ?

SCHOOLMASTER.

That is a very silly question, and whoever told
you that is a fool. The Tsar sells nothing whatsoever. A Tsar never does. As for Akulina, she
was put in prison because she was selling brandy
without a licence, and was thereby lessening the
revenues of the Crown.

MAKARKA.

How lessening ?

SCHOOLMASTER.

Because there is a duty on spirits. A barrel
costs so much in the factory, and is sold to the
public for so much more. This surplus constitutes
the income of the state. The largest revenue
comes from it, and amounts to many millions.

MAKARKA.

Then the more brandy people drink the greater
the income ?

SCHOOLMASTER.

Certainly. If it were not for that income there
would be nothing to keep the army with, or
schools, or all the rest of the things you need.

MAKARKA.

But if all those things are necessary, why not take the money directly for the necessary things? Why get it by means of brandy?

SCHOOLMASTER.

Why? because that is the law. But the children are all in now. Take your seats.

ON CAPITAL PUNISHMENT.

PETER PETROVICH, *a professor.* MARIA IVAN-OVNA, *his wife (sewing).* FEDIA, *their son, a boy of nine (listening to his father's conversation).* IVAN VASILIEVICH, *counsel for the prosecution in the court-martial.*

IVAN VASILIEVICH.

The experience of history cannot be gainsaid. We have not only seen in France after the revolution, and at other historical moments, but in our own country as well, that doing away with—I mean the removal of—perverted and dangerous members of society has, in fact, the desired result.

PETER PETROVICH.

No, we cannot know what the consequences of this are in reality. The proclamation of a state of siege is therefore not justified.

IVAN VASILIEVICH.

But neither have we the right to presume that the consequences of a state of siege must be bad, or, if it proves to be so, that such consequences are brought about by the employment of a state of siege. This is one point. The other is that fear cannot fail to influence those who have lost every human sensibility and are like beasts. What except fear could have any effect on men like that one who calmly stabbed an old woman and three children in order to steal three hundred roubles?

Peter Petrovich.

But I am not against capital punishment in principle; I am only opposed to the special courts-martial which are so often formed. If these frequent executions did nothing but inspire fear, it would be different. But in addition they pervert the mind, and killing becomes a habit of thought.

Ivan Vasilievich.

There, again, we don't know anything about the remote consequences, but we do know, on the contrary, how beneficial . . .

Peter Petrovich.

Beneficial?

Ivan Vasilievich.

Yes, how beneficial the immediate results are, and we have no right to deny it. How could society similarly fail to exact the penalty from such a wretch as . . .

PETER PETROVICH.

You mean society must take its revenge ?

IVAN VASILIEVICH.

No, the object is not revenge. On the contrary, it must substitute for personal revenge the penalty imposed for the good of the community.

PETER PETROVICH.

But in that case it must be subject to regulations settled by the law once for ever, and not as a special order of things.

IVAN VASILIEVICH.

The penalty imposed by the community is a substitute for casual, exaggerated revenge, in many cases ungrounded and erroneous, which a private individual might take.

PETER PETROVICH

(*passionately*). Do you really mean to say the penalty imposed by society is never casual, is always well founded, is never erroneous ? I cannot admit that. None of your arguments could ever convince me or any one else that this is true of a state of siege, under which thousands have been executed . . . and under which executions are still going on—that all this is both just and legal, and beneficial into the bargain! (*Rises and walks up and down in great agitation.*)

Fedia

(*to his mother*). Mother, what is father talking about?

Maria Ivanovna.

Father thinks it wrong that so many people are put to death.

Fedia.

Do you mean really put to death?

Maria Ivanovna.

Yes. He thinks it ought not to be done so frequently.

Fedia

(*coming up to his father*). Father, isn't it written in the Ten Commandments: "Thou shalt not kill"? Doesn't that mean you are not to kill at all?

Peter Petrovich

(*smiling*). That does not refer to what we are talking about. It only means that men are not to kill other men.

FEDIA.

But when they execute they kill, don't they?

PETER PETROVICH.

Certainly. But the thing is to know why and when it is permissible.

FEDIA.

When is it?

PETER PETROVICH.

Why, think of a war, or of a great villain who has committed many murders. How could one leave him unpunished?

FEDIA.

But isn't it written in the Gospel that we must love and forgive everybody?

PETER PETROVICH.

If we could do that it would be splendid. But that cannot be.

FEDIA.

Why?

PETER PETROVICH

(*to* IVAN VASILIEVICH, *who listens to* FEDIA *with a smile*). As I said, dear Ivan Vasilievich, I cannot and will not admit the benefit of a state of siege and courts-martial.

ON PRISONS.

SEMKA, *a boy of thirteen;* AKSUTKA, *a girl of ten;*
PALASHKA, *a girl of nine;* VANKA, *a boy of eight.*
They are sitting at the well, with baskets of mushrooms
which they have gathered.

AKSUTKA.

Aunt Matrena was crying so desperately. And
the children, too, would not leave off howling, all
at the same time.

VANKA.

Why were they howling?

PALASHKA.

What about? Why, their father has been taken
off to prison. Who should cry but the family?

VANKA.

Why is he in prison?

AKSUTKA.

I don't know. They came and told him to get

his things ready and led him away. We saw it all from our cottage.

SEMKA.

Serves him right for being a horse-stealer. He stole a horse from Demkin's place and one from Hramov's. He and his gang also got hold of our gelding. Who could love him for that?

AKSUTKA.

That is all right; but I am sorry for the poor brats. There are four of them. And so poor— no bread in the house. To-day they had to come to us.

SEMKA.

Serves the thief right.

MITKA.

But he's the only one that is the thief. Why must his children become beggars?

SEMKA.

Why did he steal?

MITKA.

The kids didn't steal—it is just he.

SEMKA.

Kids indeed! Why did he do wrong? That doesn't alter the case, that he has got children. Does that give him the right to be a thief?

VANKA.

What will they do to him in prison?

AKSUTKA.

He will just sit there—that's all.

VANKA.

And will they give him food?

SEMKA.

That's just the reason why they're not afraid, those damned horse-thieves! He doesn't mind going to prison. They provide him with everything, and he has nothing to do but sit idle the whole day long. If I were the Tsar, I would know how to manage those horse-thieves. . . . I would teach them a lesson that would make them give up the habit of stealing. Now he has nothing to worry him. He sits in the company of fellows like himself, and they teach each other how to steal. Grandfather said Petrusha was quite a good boy when he went to prison for the first time, but he came out a desperate villain. Since then he's taken to——

VANKA.

Then why do they put people in prison?

SEMKA.

Just ask them.

Aksutka.

He will have all his food given to him——

Semka

(*agreeing*). So he will get more accustomed to finding the food ready for him !

Aksutka.

While the kiddies and their mother have to die of starvation. They are our neighbours ; we can't help pitying them. When they come asking for bread, we can't refuse ; how could we ?

Vanka.

Then why are those people put in prison ?

Semka.

What else could be done with them ?

Vanka.

What ?—what could be done ? One must somehow manage that . . .

Semka.

Yes, somehow ! But you don't know how. There have been people with more brains than you've got who have thought about that, and they couldn't invent anything.

Palashka.

I think if I had been a queen . . .

AKSUTKA

(*laughing*).   Well, what would you have done, my queen?

PALASHKA.

I would have things so that nobody would steal and the children would not cry.

AKSUTKA.

How would you do that?

PALASHKA.

I would just see that everybody was given what he needed, that nobody was wronged by anybody else, and that they were all happy.

SEMKA.

Three cheers for the queen!   But how would you manage that?

PALASHKA.

I would just do it, you would see.

MITKA.

Let us all go to the birch woods.   The girls have been gathering a lot there lately.

SEMKA.

All right.   Come along, you fellows.—And you, queen, mind you don't drop your mushrooms. You are so sharp.   (*They get up and go away.*)

ON WEALTH.

The LANDLORD, *his* WIFE, *their* DAUGHTER *and their son* VASIA, *six years old, are having tea on the veranda. The grown-up children are playing tennis.* A YOUNG BEGGAR *comes up to the veranda.*

LANDLORD

(*to the* BEGGAR). What do you want?

BEGGAR

(*bowing to him*). I dare say you know. Have pity on a man out of work. I am tramping, with nothing to eat, and no clothes to wear. I have been to Moscow, and am trying to get home. Help a poor man.

LANDLORD.

Why are you poor?

BEGGAR.

Why? because I haven't got anything.

LANDLORD.

You would not be poor if you worked.

BEGGAR.

I would be glad to, but I can't get a job. Everything is shut down now.

LANDLORD.

How is it other people find work and you cannot ?

BEGGAR.

Believe me, upon my soul, I would be only too glad to work. But I can't find a job. Have pity on me, sir. I have not eaten for two days, and I've been tramping all the time.

LANDLORD

(*to his* WIFE, *in French*). Have you any change ? I have only notes.

HIS WIFE

(*to* VASIA). Be a good boy. Go and fetch my purse ; it is in my bag on the little table beside my bed.

> (VASIA *does not hear what his mother says; he has his eyes fixed on the* BEGGAR.)

THE WIFE.

Don't you hear, Vasia ? (*Pulling him by the sleeve.*) Vasia !

Vasia.

What, mother?

> (*The* Wife *repeats her directions.*)

Vasia

(*jumping up*). I am off. (*Goes, looking back at the* Beggar.)

Landlord

(*to the* Beggar). Wait a moment. (Beggar *steps aside.*)

Landlord

(*to his* Wife, *in French*). Is it not dreadful ? So many are out of work now. It is all laziness. Yet, it is horrid if he really is hungry.

His Wife.

I hear it is just the same abroad. I have read that in New York there are 100,000 unemployed. Another cup of tea ?

Landlord.

Yes, but much weaker. (*He lights a cigarette ; they stop talking.*)

> (Beggar *looks at them, shakes his head and coughs, evidently to attract their attention.*)

> (Vasia *comes running with the purse, looks round for the* Beggar, *and, passing the purse to his mother, looks again fixedly at the* Beggar.)

LANDLORD

(*taking a ten kopek piece out of the purse*). There, What's-your-name, take that.

BEGGAR

(*bows, pulls off his cap, and takes the money*). Thank you, thank you for that much. Many thanks for having pity on a poor man.

LANDLORD.

I pity you chiefly for being out of work. Work would save you from poverty. He who works will never be poor.

BEGGAR

(*having received the money, puts on his cap and turns away*). They say truly that work does not make a rich man but a humpback. (*Exit.*)

VASIA.

What did he say?

LANDLORD.

He repeated that stupid peasants' proverb, that work does not make a rich man but a humpback.

VASIA.

What does that mean?

LANDLORD.

It is supposed to mean that work makes a man's back crooked, without ever making him rich.

VASIA.

But that is not true, is it?

FATHER.

Of course not. Those who tramp about like that man there and have no desire to work are always poor. It's only those who work who get rich.

VASIA.

Why are we rich, then, when we don't work?

MOTHER

(*laughing*). How do you know father doesn't work?

VASIA.

I don't know, but since we are very rich, father ought to be working very hard. Is he, I wonder?

FATHER.

There is work and work. My work is perhaps work that everybody could not do.

VASIA.

What is your work?

FATHER.

My work is to provide for your food, your clothes, and your education.

VASIA.

But hasn't he to provide all that also ? Then why is he so miserable when we are so——

FATHER.

(*laughing*). What a self-made socialist, I say !

MOTHER.

Yes, people say : "A fool can ask more questions than a thousand wise men can answer." Instead of "fool," we ought to say "every child."

ON THOSE WHO OFFEND YOU.

MASHA, *a girl of ten ;* VANIA, *a boy of eight.*

MASHA.

What I wish is that mother would come home at once and take us shopping, and then to call on Nastia. What would you like to happen now?

VANIA.

I? I wish something would happen like it did yesterday.

MASHA.

What happened yesterday? You mean when Grisha hit you, and you both began to cry? There wasn't much good in that.

VANIA.

That's just what was beautiful. Nothing could have been more so. That's what I want to happen again.

MASHA.

I don't understand.

Vania.

Well, I will explain what I want. Do you remember last Sunday, Uncle P.—you know how I love him . . .

Masha.

Who wouldn't? Mother says he is a saint; and it's true.

Vania.

Well, you remember he told us a story last Sunday about a man whom people used to insult. The more any one insulted him the more he loved the offender. They abused him, and he praised them. They hit him, and he helped them. Uncle said that anybody who acts so feels very happy. I liked what he said, and I wanted to be like that man. So, when Grisha hit me yesterday, I remembered my wish and kissed Grisha. He burst out crying. I felt very happy. But with nurse yesterday it was different. She began scolding me, and I quite forgot how I ought to have behaved, and I answered her very rudely. What I wish now is to have the same experience over again that I had with Grisha.

Masha.

Then you would like somebody to strike you?

12

Vania.

I would like it awfully. I would immediately do what I did to Grisha, and I would be so glad.

Masha.

How stupid! Just like the fool you've always been.

Vania.

I don't mind being a fool. I only know now what to do so as to feel happy all the time.

Masha.

A regular fool! Do you really feel happy doing so?

Vania.

Just awfully happy!

ON THE PRESS.

The schoolroom at home.

(VOLODIA, *a schoolboy of fourteen, is reading*; SONIA, *a girl of fifteen, is writing. The* YARD-PORTER *enters, carrying a heavy load on his back*; MISHA, *a boy of eight, following him.*)

PORTER.

Where am I to put that bundle, sir? My shoulders are bent down with the weight of it.

VOLODIA.

Where were you told to put it?

PORTER.

Vasily Timofeëvich told me to carry it to the schoolroom and leave it for him.

VOLODIA.

Then put it in the corner.

(PORTER *unloads the bundle and sighs heavily.*)

SONIA.

What is it?

VOLODIA.

Truth—a paper.

MISHA.

Truth?   What do you mean?

SONIA.

Why have you so many?

VOLODIA.

It is a collection of the whole year's issues.

(*Continues reading.*)

MISHA.

Has all this been written?

PORTER.

The fellows who wrote it weren't very lazy, I'll bet.

VOLODIA

(*laughs*).   What did you say?

PORTER.

I said what I meant.   It wasn't a lazy lot that wrote all that.   Well, I'm going.   Will you kindly say I have brought the bundle?   (*Exit.*)

SONIA

(*to* VOLODIA).   What does father want all those papers for?

VOLODIA.

He wants to collect Bolchakov's articles from them.

SONIA.

And Uncle Michael Ivanovich says reading Bolchakov makes him ill.

VOLODIA.

Just like Uncle Michael Ivanovich—he only reads *Truth for All*.

MISHA.

And is uncle's *Truth* as big as this?

SONIA.

Bigger. But this is only for one year, and the papers have been published twenty years or more.

MISHA.

That makes twenty such bundles and another twenty more.

SONIA

(*wishing to mystify* MISHA). That's nothing. These are only two papers, and besides there are at least thirty more.

VOLODIA

(*without raising his head*). Thirty, you say! There are five hundred and thirty in Russia alone. And with those published abroad there are thousands altogether.

MISHA.

They couldn't all be put into this room.

VOLODIA.

Not even in this whole street. But please don't disturb me in my work. To-morrow teacher is sure to call upon me, and you don't give me a chance of learning my lessons with your silly talk.

(*Resumes his reading.*)

MISHA.

I don't think there's any use writing so much.

SONIA.

Why not ?

MISHA.

Because if what they write is true, then why say the same thing over and over again ? If it isn't, then why say what is not true ?

SONIA.

An excellent judgment !

MISHA.

Why do they write such an awful lot ?

VOLODIA

(*without taking his eyes off his book*). Because, if it wasn't for the freedom of the press, how would people know what the truth is ?

MISHA.

Father says the *Truth* contains the truth, and Uncle Michael Ivanovich says *Truth* makes him ill. Then how do they know where the truth really is—in *Truth* or in *Truth for All*?

SONIA.

I think you are right. There are really too many papers and magazines and books.

VOLODIA.

Just like a woman—perfectly senseless in every conclusion!

SONIA.

I only mean that when there is so much written it is impossible to know anything really.

VOLODIA.

But everybody has brains given him to find out where the truth is.

MISHA.

Then if everybody has got brains he can reason things out for himself.

VOLODIA.

So that's how you reason with your large supply of brains! Please go somewhere else and leave me alone to work.

ON REPENTANCE.

Volia, *a boy of eight, stands in the passage with an empty plate and cries.* Fedia, *a boy of ten, comes running into the passage.*

Fedia.

Mother sent me to see where you were; but what are you crying for? Have you brought nurse . . . (*Sees the empty plate, and whistles.*) Where is the cake?

Volia.

I—I—I wanted it, I—(*and then suddenly*)—Boo-hoo-hoo! All of a sudden I ate it up—without meaning to.

Fedia.

Instead of taking it to nurse, you have eaten it yourself on the way! Well, I never! Mother thought you wanted nurse to have the cake.

Volia.

I did (*and then suddenly, without meaning to*)— Boo-hoo-hoo!

FEDIA.

You just tasted it, and then you ate the whole of it. Well, I never ! (*Laughs.*)

VOLIA.

It is all very well for you to laugh, but how am I going to tell ? . . . Now I can't go to nurse—or to mother either.

FEDIA.

A nice mess you have made of it, I must say. Ha, ha ! So you have eaten the whole cake ? It is no use crying. Just try to think of some way of getting out of it.

VOLIA.

I can't see how I can. What shall I do ?

FEDIA.

Fancy that ! (*Trying to restrain himself from laughing. A pause.*)

VOLIA.

What am I to do now ? I am lost. (*Howls.*)

FEDIA.

Don't you care. Stop that howling. Simply go to mother and tell her you have eaten the cake yourself.

VOLIA.

That is worse.

12 *a*

FEDIA.

Then go and confess to nurse.

VOLIA.

How can I ?

FEDIA.

Listen ; you wait here. I will find nurse and tell her. She won't mind.

VOLIA.

No, don't ; I cannot let her know about it.

FEDIA.

Nonsense. You did it by mistake ; it can't be helped. I will tell her in a minute. (*Runs away.*)

VOLIA.

Fedia, Fedia, wait ! He is gone. I just tasted it, and then I don't remember how I did it. What am I to do now ! (*Sobbing.*)

FEDIA.

(*comes running back*). Stop your bawling, I say. I told you nurse would forgive you. She only said, " Oh, the darling ! "

VOLIA.

She is not cross with me ?

FEDIA.

Not a bit. She said, "I don't care for the cake ; I would have given it to him anyhow."

VOLIA.

But I didn't mean to eat it. (*Cries again.*)

FEDIA.

Why are you crying again ? We won't tell mother. Nurse has quite forgiven you.

VOLIA.

Nurse has forgiven me. I know she is kind and good. But me—I am a wicked boy, and that's what makes me cry.

ON ART.

FOOTMAN; HOUSEKEEPER; NATASHA (*a little girl*).

FOOTMAN

(*with a tray*). Almond milk for the tea, and rum——

HOUSEKEEPER

(*knitting a stocking and counting the stitches*). Twenty-three, twenty-four——

FOOTMAN.

I say, Avdotia Vasilievna, can't you hear?

HOUSEKEEPER.

I hear, I hear. I'll give it to you presently. I can't tear myself to pieces to do all kinds of work at the same moment. (*To* NATASHA) Yes, darling; I will bring you the prunes presently. Just wait a moment, till I have given him the milk. (*Strains the almond milk.*)

FOOTMAN

(*sitting down*). I tell you I have seen something

to-night. To think that they pay good money for that!

HOUSEKEEPER.

Oh, you have been to the theatre. You were out late to-night.

FOOTMAN.

An opera is always a long affair. I have always to wait hours and hours. To-night they were kind, and let me in to see the performance.

(*The manservant* PAVEL *enters with the cream, and stands listening.*)

HOUSEKEEPER.

Then there was singing to-night?

FOOTMAN.

Singing—humph! Just silly, loud screaming, not a bit like real singing. "I," he said—"I love her so much." And he puts it all to a tune, and it is not like anything under heaven. Then they had a row, and ought to have fought it out; but they started singing instead.

HOUSEKEEPER.

And yet I've heard it costs a lot to get seats for the season.

FOOTMAN.

Our box cost three hundred roubles for twelve nights.

PAVEL.

(*shaking his head*). Three hundred! And who does that money go to?

FOOTMAN.

Why, the people who sing are paid for it. I was told a lady singer makes fifty thousand a year.

PAVEL.

You talk of thousands! why, three hundred is a pile of money in the country. Some folks toil their whole life long, and can't even get together one hundred.

> (NINA, *a schoolgirl, enters the servants' pantry.*)

NINA.

Is Natasha here?—Why don't you come? Mother wants you.

NATASHA

(*munching a prune*). I am coming.

NINA

(*to* PAVEL). What were you saying about a hundred roubles?

Housekeeper.

Simeon (*pointing to the footman*) was just telling us about the singing he listened to to-night in the theatre, and about the lady singers being paid such a lot of money. That's what made Pavel wonder. Is that really true, Nina Mikhailovna, that a lady may get fifty thousand for her singing?

Nina.

More than that. A lady has been engaged to sing in America for a hundred and fifty thousand roubles. But even better than that, yesterday's paper says a musician has been paid fifty thousand roubles for his finger-nail.

Pavel.

The papers write all sorts of nonsense. That couldn't be. How could he be paid that?

Nina

(*evidently pleased*). He was, I tell you.

Pavel.

Just for a finger-nail?

Natasha.

How is that possible?

NINA.

He was a pianist, and was insured for that amount in case anything happened to his hand and he couldn't go on playing the piano.

PAVEL.

Well, I'll be blowed!

SENICHKA

(*a schoolboy in the upper class of the school, entering the pantry*). You've got a regular meeting here. What is it all about?

> (NINA *tells him what they have been talking about.*)

SENICHKA

(*with still more complacency than* NINA). That story of the nail is nothing at all. Why, a dancer in Paris had her foot insured for two hundred thousand roubles, in case she sprained it and was not able to go on dancing.

FOOTMAN.

That's them girls—excuse me for mentioning it—that work with their legs without any stockings on.

PAVEL.

You call that work! And they are paid for it!

SENICHKA.

But every one cannot do that kind of work; and she had to study a good many years.

PAVEL.

What did she study that did any good? Mere hopping about?

SENICHKA.

You don't understand. Art is a great thing.

PAVEL.

I think it is all nonsense. People spend money like that because they have such an easy time. If they had to bend their backs as we do to make a living, there wouldn't be all these singing and dancing girls. They ain't worth anything — but what is the use of saying so?

SENICHKA.

There we have the outcome of ignorance. To him Beethoven and Viardot and Rafael are utter folly.

NATASHA.

Well, I think what he says is so.

NINA.

Come, let's go.

ON SCIENCE.

Two schoolboys—one a pupil of the real gymnasium,* and the other of the classical gymnasium; two twins, brothers of the latter, VOLODIA *and* PETRUSHA, *eight years of age.*

SCIENCE SCHOLAR.

What do I want with Latin and Greek, when everything of any value has been translated into the modern languages?

CLASSICAL SCHOLAR.

You will never understand the *Iliad* unless you read it in Greek.

SCIENCE SCHOLAR.

But I don't see the use of reading it. I don't want to.

VOLODIA.

What is the *Iliad?*

SCIENCE SCHOLAR.

A story.

---

* A school for natural science without Greek and Latin; in the classical gymnasium Latin and Greek are taught.

CLASSICAL SCHOLAR.

Yes, a story, but one that has not its equal in the world.

PETRUSHA.

What is it that makes that story so particularly good?

SCIENCE SCHOLAR.

Nothing. It is just a story, and nothing else.

CLASSICAL SCHOLAR.

Yes; but you cannot really understand antiquity without a knowledge of this story.

SCIENCE SCHOLAR.

I consider that a superstition just like religious instruction.

CLASSICAL SCHOLAR

(*getting excited*). Religious instruction is nothing but lies and nonsense, while this is history and wisdom.

VOLODIA.

Is religious instruction all nonsense?

CLASSICAL SCHOLAR.

Why do you sit there listening to our talk? You can't understand.

BOTH BOYS

(*hurt*). Why shouldn't we?

VOLODIA.

Perhaps we understand things better than you do.

CLASSICAL SCHOLAR.

Very well. Just be quiet, and don't interrupt. (*To the* SCIENCE SCHOLAR.) You say Latin and Greek are of no use in life; but that applies as well to bacteriology, to chemistry, to physics, and astronomy. Why is it necessary to know anything about the distance of the stars, about their size, and all those unnecessary details?

SCIENCE SCHOLAR.

Unnecessary? On the contrary, they are very necessary indeed.

CLASSICAL SCHOLAR.

What for?

SCIENCE SCHOLAR.

Why, for everything. Take navigation. You would think that had not much to do with astronomy. But look at the practical results of science—the way it is applied to agriculture, to medicine, to the industries——

CLASSICAL SCHOLAR.

On the other hand, it is used also in making bombs, for purposes of war, and for revolutionary objects as well. If science contributed to the moral improvement, then——

SCIENCE SCHOLAR.

But what about your sort of knowledge? Does that raise the moral standard?

VOLODIA.

Is there any science that makes people better?

CLASSICAL SCHOLAR.

I told you not to interfere in the discussions of grown-up people. You say nothing but silly things.

VOLODIA *and* PETRUSHA.

(*with one voice*). Not so silly as you imagine. . . . Just tell us which science teaches people how to be good.

SCIENCE SCHOLAR.

There isn't such a science. Everybody has to find that out for himself.

CLASSICAL SCHOLAR.

What is the use of talking to them? They don't understand.

SCIENCE SCHOLAR.

Why not? They might. How to be good, Volodia and Petrusha, is not taught in schools.

VOLODIA.

Well, if that is not taught, it is no use going to school.

PETRUSHA.

When we are grown up we will not learn useless things.

VOLODIA.

As for the right way to live, we'll do that better than you.

CLASSICAL SCHOLAR

(*laughing*).   Oh, the wisdom of that conclusion!

ON GOING TO LAW.

A PEASANT, *his* WIFE, *a* KINSWOMAN, FEDIA, *the peasant's son, a lad of nineteen.* PETKA, *another son, a boy of nine.*

PEASANT

(*entering the cottage and taking off his cloak*). What beastly weather! I could hardly manage to get home.

WIFE.

And such a long way for you. It must be nearly fifteen miles.

PEASANT.

Not less than twenty, I can tell you. (*To his son,* FEDIA) Take the colt to the stable.

WIFE.

Well, have we won?

PEASANT.

We have not, damn it all. It will never come right.

Kinswoman.

But what is it all about, cousin ? I don't quite understand.

Peasant.

It is simply that Averian has taken possession of my vegetable garden and is holding it. And I can't get at him in the right way.

Wife.

That lawsuit has been dragging along over a year now.

Kinswoman.

I know, I know. I remember as far back as Lent, when the matter was before the village court. My man told me it had been settled in your favour.

Peasant.

That finished it, didn't it ? But Averian appealed to the head of the Zemstvo,* and he had the whole business gone into again. I then appealed to the judge, and won. That ought to have been the end of it. But it wasn't. After that he won. Nice sort of judges they are !

Wife.

What are we to do now ?

* County council.

Peasant.

I won't stand his having my property ; I will appeal to the higher court. I have already had a talk with a lawyer.

Kinswoman.

But suppose they take his side in the upper court ?

Peasant.

Then I'll go to the Supreme Court. I'll sell my last cow before I'll give in to that fat hound. I'll teach him a lesson.

Kinswoman.

A lot of trouble comes from these trials, a lot of trouble, I declare ! And suppose he wins again ?

Peasant.

Then I'll appeal to the Tsar. Now I had better go out and give the pony some hay. (*Exit.*)

Petka.

Why do they judge like that, some saying Averian is right and some daddy ?

Mother.

Probably because they don't know who is right themselves.

Petka.

Then why ask them, if they don't know?

Mother.

Because nobody wants to give up his property.

Petka.

When I grow up I will do like this : If I have a dispute with somebody, we will cast lots and see who wins. And that will settle it. We always settle it this way with Akulika.

Kinswoman.

Don't you think, cousin, that is quite a good way? One sin less, anyhow.

Mother.

Quite so. What a lot we have spent on that trial! more than the whole vegetable garden is worth. Oh, it is a sin, a great sin!

ON THE CRIMINAL COURT.

Children : GRISHKA, SEMKA, JISHKA.

JISHKA.

Serves him right. Why did he make his way into another person's corn loft? When he is put in prison that will teach him not to do it another time.

SEMKA.

Of course, if he has really done it. But old Mikita said Mitrofan was run into prison without being guilty.

JISHKA.

Without being guilty? And won't anything happen to the man who judged him falsely?

GRISHKA.

Well, they won't pat him on the head for it, of course. If he hasn't judged according to law he will be punished too.

SEMKA.

Who will punish him?

JISHKA.

Those above him.

SEMKA.

Who are above him?

GRISHKA.

His superiors.

JISHKA.

And if the superiors also make a mistake?

GRISHKA.

There are higher powers above them, and they will be punished by these. That's what the Tsar is for.

JISHKA.

But if the Tsar judges wrong, who is going to punish him?

GRISHKA.

Who? Why do you ask that? Don't you know?

SEMKA.

God will punish him.

JISHKA.

God will also punish him who stole the corn from the loft. Then why not leave it to God to punish those who are guilty ?   He will not judge wrong.

GRISHKA.

It's clear that that is not possible.

JISHKA.

Why not ?

GRISHKA.

Because . . .

ON PROPERTY.

An old carpenter is mending the railings on a veranda. A boy of seven, the son of the master of the house, is watching the man working.

BOY.

How well you work ! What is your name ?

CARPENTER.

My name ? They used to call me Hrolka, and now they call me Hrol, and even Hrol Savich* when they speak respectfully.

BOY.

How well you work, Frol Savich !

CARPENTER.

As long as you have to work you may as well do good work.

BOY.

Have you got a veranda in your house ?

---

* The name is *Frol*, but the common way of the ignorant masses is to use *H* instead of *F*. It is as if one said Johnny, then John, and then John Smith.

CARPENTER.

In our house ? We have a veranda, my boy ; yours here is nothing to compare with it. A veranda with no windows. And if you step on to it, well, you can't believe your eyes. That's the kind of veranda we've got.

BOY.

You are making fun. No, seriously, tell me : have you a veranda like this ? I want to know.

CARPENTER.

My dear child, how can the likes of us have a veranda ? It's a blessing if we've a roof over our heads ; and you say, "a veranda" ! I've been thinking about having a roof built ever since last spring. I've just managed to pull down the old one ; but the new one isn't finished, and the house is standing there and getting damp without it.

BOY

(*surprised*). But why ?

CARPENTER.

Why ? Just because I am not able to do it.

BOY.

How so, if you are able to work for us ?

CARPENTER.

I can work all right for you, but not for myself.

BOY.

Why? I can't understand. Please explain.

CARPENTER.

You will understand when you are grown up. I am able to do your work, but as for my own, I can't do it.

BOY.

But why?

CARPENTER.

Because I need wood for that, and I haven't got any. It has to be bought. I have nothing to buy it with. When I have finished my work here and your mother pays me, just you tell her to pay me well. Then I'll drive to the forest, get five ash trees or so to bring home, and finish my roof.

BOY.

Do you mean you haven't a forest of your own?

CARPENTER.

We have such big forests that you can walk three whole days and not reach the end. But, worse luck, they don't belong to us.

Boy.

Mother says all her trouble comes from our forest ; she has continual worries about it.

Carpenter.

That's the worst of it.   Your mother is worried by having too much wood, and I'm worried by having none at all.   But here I am gabbling with you and forgetting my work.   And the likes of us don't get made much of for doing that.

(Resumes his work.)

Boy.

When I grow up I shall arrange to have just the same as everybody else, so that all of us are equal.

Carpenter.

Mind you grow up quickly, that I may still be alive.   Then, mind you don't forget. . . . Where have I put my plane ?

ON CHILDREN.

A LADY *with her children—a* SCHOOLBOY *of four-teen, a girl of five,* JANICHKA *— is walking in the garden. An* OLD PEASANT WOMAN *approaches them.*

LADY.

What do you want, Matresha?

OLD WOMAN.

I have come again to ask a favour of your lady-ship.

LADY.

What is it?

OLD WOMAN.

I am simply ashamed to speak, your ladyship, but that don't help. My daughter, the one for whom you stood godmother, has got another baby. God has given her a boy this time. She sent me to ask your ladyship if you would do her a favour, and have the child christened into our Orthodox faith.*

---

* When a lady in Russia stands godmother she gives the christening robes and a dress to the mother. The godfather pays the priest and gives his godchild a cross.

Lady.

But didn't she have a child very recently?

Old Woman.

Well, that's just as you think. A year ago in Lent.

Lady.

How many grandchildren have you got now?

Old Woman.

I could hardly tell you, dear lady. All of them are still babes. Such a misfortune!

Lady.

How many children has your daughter?

Old Woman.

This is the seventh child, your ladyship, and all alive. I wish God had taken some back to Him.

Lady.

How can you speak like that?

Old Woman.

I can't help it. That's how one comes to sin. But then our misery is so great. Well, your ladyship, are you willing to help us, and stand godmother to the child? Believe me, on my soul, lady, we have not even got anything to pay the priest ; bread itself is scarce in the house. All the children are small. My son-in-law is working away from home, and I am alone with my daughter. I am old, and she is expecting or nursing the whole time, and what work can you ask her to do with all that ? So it is me that has to do everything ; and that hungry lot all the while asking for food.

LADY.

Are there really seven children ?

OLD WOMAN.

Seven, your ladyship, sure. Just the eldest girl begins to help a bit ; all the rest are little.

LADY.

But why do they have such a lot of children ?

OLD WOMAN.

How can one help that, dear lady ? He comes now and then for a short stay, or just for a feast day. They are young, and he lives near in town. I wish he had to go somewhere far away.

LADY.

That's the way ! Some people are sad because

they have no children, or their children die, and you complain of having too many.

OLD WOMAN.

They are too many. We have not the means to keep them. Well, your ladyship, may I cheer her up with your consent?

LADY.

Well, I will stand godmother to this one like the others. It is a boy, you say?

OLD WOMAN.

It's a small baby, but very strong; he's got good lungs. What day do you order the christening to be?

LADY.

Whenever you like.

(OLD WOMAN *thanks her and goes.*)

JANICHKA.

Mother, why is it that some people have children and some have not? You have, Matresha has, but Parasha hasn't any.

LADY.

Parasha is not married. People have children when they are married. They marry, become husband and wife, and then only children come.

Janichka.

Do they always get children then?

Lady.

No, not always. Our cook has a wife, but they have no children.

Janichka.

Couldn't it be arranged that only those who want children should have them, and those who don't want them should have none?

Schoolboy.

What nonsense you talk!

Janichka.

That is not nonsense at all. I only thought that if Matresha's daughter doesn't want to have children, it ought to be arranged so that she shouldn't have any. Couldn't it be arranged, mother?

Schoolboy.

Have I not told you not to talk nonsense about things you know nothing about?

Janichka.

Mother, could it be arranged as I say?

Lady.

I don't know; we never know about that. It all depends on the will of God.

JANICHKA.

But how do children come into the world?

SCHOOLBOY.

The goat brings them.

JANICHKA

(*hurt*). Why do you tease me? I don't see anything to laugh at in what I am saying. But I do think that, since Matresha says they are worse off for having children, it ought to be managed so that no children should be born to her. There is Nurse who has none.

LADY.

But she is not married.

JANICHKA.

Then all those that do not care for children ought not to marry. As it is now, children are born and people have nothing to feed them with. (*The mother exchanges a glance with her son, and does not answer.*) When I am grown up I will marry by all means, and I shall see that I have one girl and one boy, and no more. Do you think it is nice when children are born and people don't care for them? As for mine, I shall love them dearly. Don't you think so, mother? I will go and ask Nurse. (*Exit.*)

LADY

(*to her son*). Yes, truth flows from the lips of children. What she says is a great truth. If people would understand how serious marriage is, instead of regarding it as amusement—if they would marry not for their own sake, but for the sake of the children—then all these horrors would not exist. There would be no children suffering from neglect or distress, nor would such cases happen as that of Matresha's daughter, where children bring sorrow in place of joy.

ON EDUCATION.

The YARD PORTER *is cleaning the handles of the doors.* KATIA, *a girl of seven, is building a house with blocks.* NICHOLAS, *a schoolboy of fifteen, enters with a book and throws it angrily on the floor.*

NICHOLAS.
To the devil with that damned school !

PORTER.
What is the matter with it ?

NICHOLAS.
Again a bad mark. That means more new trouble. Damn it all ! What do I want their cursed geography for ? California—why is it necessary to know about California ?

PORTER.
What will they do to you ?

NICHOLAS.
They will keep me another year in that same old class.

13 *a*

PORTER.

Then why don't you learn your lessons?

NICHOLAS.

Why? Because I can't learn the stupid things. Damn it all! (*Throwing himself on a chair.*) I'll go and tell mother. I'll tell her I can't do it. Let them do whatever they like, but I can't do it. And if after that she doesn't take me out of school I will run away from home. I swear I will.

PORTER.

But where will you go?

NICHOLAS.

Just away. I will look out for a place as a coachman or a yard porter. Anything is better than having to learn that cursed nonsense.

PORTER.

But to be a yard porter is not an easy job either, I can tell you. A porter has to get up early, chop wood, carry it in, make fires——

NICHOLAS.

Whew! (*Whistles.*) But that is like a holiday. I love chopping wood—I simply adore it. No, that would not stop me. No, you just try what it is to learn geography.

PORTER.

You're right there. But why do you learn it? What use is it to you? Is it that they make you do it?

NICHOLAS.

I wish I knew why. It is of no use whatever. But that's the rule. They think one cannot do without it.

PORTER.

I dare say it is necessary for you in order to become an official, to get honours, high appointments, like your father and uncle.

NICHOLAS.

But since I don't care for all that !

KATIA.

Since he does not care !

> (*Enter* MOTHER, *with a letter in her hand.*)

MOTHER.

I have just heard from the director of the school that you have got a bad mark again. That won't do, Nikolenka. It must be one thing or the other—learn or not learn.

NICHOLAS.

I'll stick to the one : I cannot, I cannot, I cannot learn. For God's sake, let me go. I cannot learn.

MOTHER.

You cannot learn?

NICHOLAS.

I cannot. It won't get into my head.

MOTHER.

That is because your head is full of nonsense. Don't think about all your stupid things, but concentrate your mind on the lessons you have to learn.

NICHOLAS.

Mother, I am talking seriously. Take me away from school. I wish for nothing else in the world but to get rid of that dreadful school, of that treadmill! I can't stand it.

MOTHER.

But what would you do out of school?

NICHOLAS.

That is my own business.

MOTHER.

It is not your own business, but mine. I have to answer to God for you. I must give you an education.

NICHOLAS.

But since I cannot.

MOTHER

(*severely*). What nonsense to say you cannot! For the last time, I will speak to you like a mother. I beseech you to mend your ways and to do what is required of you. If you will not obey me this time I shall take other measures.

NICHOLAS.

I tell you, I cannot and I will not learn.

MOTHER.

Take care, Nicholas.

NICHOLAS.

Why should I take care? Why do you torture me? Don't you see you do!

MOTHER.

I forbid you to speak like that. How dare you! Go away! You will see——

NICHOLAS.

Very well—I *will* go. I am not afraid of whatever comes, and I don't want anything from you. (*Dashes out of the room and bangs the door.*)

Mother

(*to herself*). How unhappy he makes me! I know exactly how it has all come about. It is all because he does not think about the things he ought to do, and his head is full of nothing but his own stupid interests—his dogs and his hens.

Katia.

But, mother, you remember the tale you told me : how impossible it is not to think about the white polar bear when you are told not to.

Mother.

I am not speaking of that ; I say a boy has to learn when he is told to.

Katia.

But he says he cannot.

Mother.

That's nonsense.

Katia.

But he does not say he is not willing to do any work whatever ; he only objects to learning geography. He wants to work—to be a coachman, a yard porter.

Mother.

If he had been a yard porter's son he might

become one himself; but being your father's son he must learn.

KATIA.

But he does not want to.

MOTHER.

Whether he wants to or not he must obey.

KATIA.

And if he simply cannot learn?

MOTHER.

Take care that you are not like him yourself.

KATIA.

That's just what I want to be. I shall not, on any condition, learn what I do not wish to.

MOTHER.

Then you will grow up a fool.

KATIA.

And when I am grown up and have children, I will never compel them to learn. If they want to, they may learn; if not, let them do without learning.

MOTHER.

When you are grown up, you will be sure to have changed your mind.

KATIA.

I shall certainly not.

MOTHER.

You will.

KATIA.

No, I shall not, I shall not.

MOTHER.

Then you will be a fool.

KATIA.

Nurse says God wants fools also.

THE YOUNG TSAR.

THE YOUNG TSAR.

THE young Tsar had just ascended the throne. For five weeks he had worked without ceasing, in the way that Tsars are accustomed to work. He had been attending to reports, signing papers, receiving ambassadors and high officials who came to be presented to him, and reviewing troops. He was tired, and as a traveller exhausted by heat and thirst longs for a draught of water and for rest, so he longed for a respite of just one day at least from receptions, from speeches, from parades—a few free hours to spend like an ordinary human being with his young, clever, and beautiful wife, to whom he had been married only a month before.

It was Christmas Eve. The young Tsar had arranged to have a complete rest that evening. The night before he had worked till very late at documents which his ministers of state had left for him to examine. In the morning he was present at the *Te Deum*, and then at a military service. In the afternoon he received official visitors; and later he had been obliged to listen to the reports of three ministers of state, and had given his assent to many important matters. In his conference with the Minister of Finance he had agreed to an increase of duties on imported goods, which should in the future add many millions to the State revenues. Then he sanctioned the sale of brandy by the Crown in various parts of the country, and signed a decree permitting the sale of alcohol in villages having markets. This was also calculated to increase the principal revenue to the State, which was derived from the sale of spirits. He had also approved of the issuing of a new gold loan required for a financial negotiation. The Minister of Justice having reported on the complicated case of the succession of the Baron Snyders, the young Tsar confirmed the decision by his signature; and also approved the new rules relating to the application of Article 1830 of the penal code, providing for the punishment of tramps. In his conference with the Minister of the Interior he ratified the order concerning the collection of taxes in arrears, signed the order settling what measures should be taken in regard to the persecution of religious dissenters, and also one providing for the continuance of martial law in those provinces where it had already been established. With the

Minister of War he arranged for the nomination of a new Corps Commander for the raising of recruits, and for punishment of breach of discipline. These things kept him occupied till dinner-time, and even then his freedom was not complete. A number of high officials had been invited to dinner, and he was obliged to talk to them: not in the way he felt disposed to do, but according to what he was expected to say. At last the tiresome dinner was over, and the guests departed.

The young Tsar heaved a sigh of relief, stretched himself and retired to his apartments to take off his uniform with the decorations on it, and to don the jacket he used to wear before his accession to the throne. His young wife had also retired to take off her dinner-dress, remarking that she would join him presently.

When he had passed the row of footmen who were standing erect before him, and reached his room; when he had thrown off his heavy uniform and put on his jacket, the young Tsar felt glad to be free from work; and his heart was filled with a tender emotion which sprang from the consciousness of his freedom, of his joyous, robust young life, and of his love. He threw himself on the sofa, stretched out his legs upon it, leaned his head on his hand, fixed his gaze on the dull glass shade of the lamp, and then a sensation which he had not experienced since his childhood—the pleasure of going to sleep, and a drowsiness that was irresistible—suddenly came over him.

"My wife will be here presently and will find me asleep. No, I must not go to sleep," he thought. He let his elbow drop down, laid his cheek in the palm of his hand, made himself comfortable, and was so utterly happy that he only felt a desire not to be aroused from this delightful state.

And then what happens to all of us every day happened to him—he fell asleep without knowing himself when or how. He passed from one state into another without his will having any share in it, without even desiring it, and without regretting the state out of which he had passed. He fell into a heavy sleep which was like death. How long he had slept he did not know, but he was suddenly aroused by the soft touch of a hand upon his shoulder.

"It is my darling, it is she," he thought. "What a shame to have dozed off!"

But it was not she. Before his eyes, which were wide open and blinking at the light, she, that charming and beautiful creature whom he was expecting, did not stand, but *he* stood. Who *he* was the young Tsar did not know, but somehow it did not strike him that he was a stranger whom he had never seen before. It seemed as if he had known him for a long time and was fond of him, and as if he trusted him as he would trust himself. He had expected his beloved wife, but in her stead that man whom he had never seen before had come. Yet to the young Tsar, who was far from feeling regret or astonishment, it seemed not only a most natural, but also a necessary thing to happen.

" Come ! " said the stranger.

" Yes, let us go," said the young Tsar, not knowing where he was to go, but quite aware that he could not help submitting to the command of the stranger. " But how shall we go ?" he asked.

" In this way."

The stranger laid his hand on the Tsar's head, and the Tsar for a moment lost consciousness. He could not tell whether he had been unconscious a long or a short time, but when he recovered his senses he found himself in a strange place. The first thing he was aware of was a strong and stifling smell of sewage. The place in which he stood was a broad passage lit by the red glow of two dim lamps. Running along one side of the passage was a thick wall with windows protected by iron gratings. On the other side were doors secured with locks. In the passage stood a soldier, leaning up against the wall, asleep. Through the doors the young Tsar heard the muffled sound of living human beings : not of one alone, but of many. *He* was standing at the side of the young Tsar, and pressing his shoulder slightly with his soft hand, pushed him to the first door, unmindful of the sentry. The young Tsar felt he could not do otherwise than yield, and approached the door. To his amazement the sentry looked straight at him, evidently without seeing him, as he neither straightened himself up nor saluted, but yawned loudly and, lifting his hand, scratched the back of his neck. The door had a small hole, and in obedience to the pressure of the hand that pushed him, the young Tsar approached a step nearer and put his eye to the small opening. Close to the door, the foul smell that stifled him was stronger, and the young Tsar hesitated to go nearer, but the hand pushed him on. He leaned forward, put his eye close to the opening, and suddenly ceased to perceive the odour. The sight he saw deadened his sense of smell. In a large room, about ten yards long and six yards wide, there walked unceasingly from one end to the other six men in long gray coats, some in felt boots, some barefoot. There were over twenty men in all in the room, but in that first moment the young Tsar only saw those who were walking with quick, even, silent steps. It was a horrid sight to watch the continual, quick, aimless movements of the men who passed and overtook each other, turning sharply when they reached the wall, never looking at one another, and evidently concentrated each on his own thoughts. The young Tsar had observed a similar sight one day when he was watching a tiger in a menagerie pacing rapidly with noiseless tread from one end of his cage to the other, waving its tail, silently turning when it reached the bars, and looking at nobody. Of these men one, apparently a young peasant, with curly hair, would have been handsome were it not for the unnatural pallor of his face, and the concentrated, wicked, scarcely human, look in his eyes. Another was a Jew, hairy and gloomy. The third was a lean old man, bald, with a beard that had been shaven and had since grown like bristles. The fourth was extraordinarily heavily built, with well-developed muscles, a low receding forehead, and a flat nose. The fifth was hardly more than a boy, long, thin, obviously consumptive. The sixth was small and dark, with nervous, convulsive movements. He walked as if he were skipping, and muttered continuously to himself. They were all walking rapidly backwards and forwards past

the hole through which the young Tsar was looking. He watched their faces and their gait with
keen interest. Having examined them closely, he
presently became aware of a number of other men
at the back of the room, standing round, or lying
on the shelf that served as a bed. Standing close
to the door he also saw the pail which caused
such an unbearable stench. On the shelf about
ten men, entirely covered with their cloaks, were
sleeping. A red-haired man with a huge beard
was sitting sideways on the shelf, with his shirt
off. He was examining it, lifting it up to the
light, and evidently catching the vermin on it.
Another man, aged and white as snow, stood with
his profile turned towards the door. He was praying, crossing himself, and bowing low, apparently
so absorbed in his devotions as to be oblivious of
all around him.

"I see—this is a prison," thought the young
Tsar. "They certainly deserve pity. It is a
dreadful life. But it cannot be helped. It is
their own fault."

But this thought had hardly come into his head
before *he*, who was his guide, replied to it.

"They are all here under lock and key by your
order. They have all been sentenced in your name.
But far from meriting their present condition which
is due to your human judgment, the greater part

of them are far better than you or those who were
their judges and who keep them here. This one "
—he pointed to the handsome, curly-headed fellow
—" is a murderer. I do not consider him more
guilty than those who kill in war or in duelling,
and are rewarded for their deeds. He had neither
education nor moral guidance, and his life had been
cast among thieves and drunkards. This lessens
his guilt, but he has done wrong, nevertheless, in
being a murderer. He killed a merchant, to rob
him. The other man, the Jew, is a thief, one of a
gang of thieves. That uncommonly strong fellow
is a horse-stealer, and guilty also, but compared
with others not as culpable. Look !"—and suddenly the young Tsar found himself in an open
field on a vast frontier. On the right were potato-
fields ; the plants had been rooted out, and were
lying in heaps, blackened by the frost ; in alternate
streaks were rows of winter corn. In the distance
a little village with its tiled roofs was visible ; on
the left were fields of winter corn and fields of
stubble. No one was to be seen on any side, save a
black human figure in front at the border-line, a gun
slung on his back, and at his feet a dog. On the
spot where the young Tsar stood, sitting beside
him, almost at his feet, was a young Russian
soldier with a green band on his cap, and with his
rifle slung over his shoulders, who was rolling up

a paper to make a cigarette. The soldier was obviously unaware of the presence of the young Tsar and his companion, and had not heard them. He did turn round when the Tsar, who was standing directly over the soldier, asked, "Where are we?" "On the Prussian frontier," his guide answered. Suddenly, far away in front of them, a shot was fired. The soldier jumped to his feet, and seeing two men running, bent low to the ground, hastily put his tobacco into his pocket and ran after one of them. "Stop, or I'll shoot!" cried the soldier. The fugitive, without stopping, turned his head and called out something evidently abusive or blasphemous. "Damn you!" shouted the soldier, who put one foot a little forward and stopped, after which, bending his head over his rifle and raising his right hand, he rapidly adjusted something, took aim, and, pointing the gun in the direction of the fugitive, probably fired, although no sound was heard. "Smokeless powder, no doubt," thought the young Tsar, and looking after the fleeing man saw him take a few hurried steps and, bending lower and lower, fall to the ground and crawl on his hands and knees. At last he remained lying and did not move. The other fugitive, who was ahead of him, turned round and ran back to the man who was lying on the ground.   He did something for him and then resumed his flight.

" What does all this mean ? " asked the Tsar.

" These are the guards on the frontier, enforcing the revenue laws.   That man was killed to protect the revenues of the State."

" Has he actually been killed ? "

The guide again laid his hand upon the head of the young Tsar, and again the Tsar lost consciousness.   When he had recovered his senses he found himself in a small room—the customs office. The dead body of a man, with a thin grizzled beard, an aquiline nose, and big eyes with the eyelids closed, was lying on the floor.   His arms were thrown asunder, his feet bare, and his thick, dirty toes were turned up at right angles and stuck out straight.   He had a wound in his side, and on his ragged cloth jacket as well as on his blue shirt were stains of clotted blood, which had turned black save for a few red spots here and there.   A woman stood close to the wall, so wrapped up in shawls that her face could scarcely be seen.   Motionless she gazed at the aquiline nose, the upturned feet, and the protruding eyeballs ; sobbing and sighing, and drying her tears at long, regular intervals.   A pretty girl of thirteen was standing at her mother's side, with her eyes and mouth wide open.   A boy of eight clung to his mother's skirt, and looked intently at his dead father without blinking.

From a door near them an official, an officer, a doctor, and a clerk with documents, entered. After them came a soldier, the one who had shot the man. He stepped briskly along behind his superiors, but the instant he saw the corpse he went suddenly pale, and quivered; and, dropping his head, stood still. When the official asked him whether that was the man who was escaping across the frontier, and at whom he had fired, he was unable to answer. His lips trembled, and his face twitched. "The s—s—s—" he began, but could not get out the words which he wanted to say. "The same, your excellency." The officials looked at each other and wrote something down.

"You see the beneficial results of that same system!"

In a room of sumptuous vulgarity two men sat drinking wine. One of them was old and gray, the other a young Jew. The young Jew was holding a roll of bank-notes in his hand, and was bargaining with the old man. He was buying smuggled goods.

"You've got 'em cheap," he said, smiling.

"Yes—but the risk——"

"This is indeed terrible," said the young Tsar;

"but it cannot be avoided. Such proceedings are necessary."

His companion made no response, saying merely, "Let us move on," and laid his hand again on the head of the Tsar. When the Tsar recovered consciousness he was standing in a small room lit by a shaded lamp. A woman was sitting at the table sewing. A boy of eight was bending over the table, drawing, with his feet doubled up under him in the arm-chair. A student was reading aloud. The father and daughter of the family entered the room noisily.

"You signed the order concerning the sale of spirits," said the guide to the Tsar.

"Well?" said the woman.

"He's not likely to live."

"What's the matter with him?"

"They've kept him drunk all the time."

"It's not possible!" exclaimed the wife.

"It's true. And the boy's only nine years old, that Vania Moroshkine."

"What did you do to try to save him?" asked the wife.

"I tried everything that could be done. I gave him an emetic and put a mustard-plaster on him. He has every symptom of delirium tremens."

"It's no wonder—the whole family are drunkards. Annisia is only a little better than the rest, and even she is generally more or less drunk," said the daughter.

"And what about your temperance society?" the student asked his sister.

"What can we do when they are given every opportunity of drinking? Father tried to have the public-house shut up, but the law is against him. And besides, when I was trying to convince Vasily Ermiline that it was disgraceful to keep a public-house and ruin the people with drink, he answered very haughtily, and indeed got the better of me before the crowd: 'But I have a licence with the Imperial eagle on it. If there was anything wrong in my business, the Tsar wouldn't have issued a decree authorizing it.' Isn't it terrible? The whole village has been drunk for the last three days. And as for feast-days, it is simply horrible to think of! It has been proved conclusively that alcohol does no good in any case, but invariably does harm, and it has been demonstrated to be an absolute poison. Then, ninety-nine per cent. of the crimes in the world are committed through its influence. We all know how the standard of morality and the general welfare improved at once in all the countries where drinking has been suppressed—like Sweden and Finland, and we know that it can be suppressed by exercising a moral influence over the masses.   But in our country the class which could exert that influence—the Government, the Tsar and his officials—simply encourage drink. Their main revenues are drawn from the continual drunkenness of the people.   They drink themselves—they are always drinking the health of somebody : 'Gentlemen, the Regiment !'   The preachers drink, the bishops drink——"

Again the guide touched the head of the young Tsar, who again lost consciousness.   This time he found himself in a peasant's cottage.   The peasant—a man of forty, with red face and bloodshot eyes—was furiously striking the face of an old man, who tried in vain to protect himself from the blows.   The younger peasant seized the beard of the old man and held it fast.

"For shame !   To strike your father—— !"

"I don't care, I'll kill him !   Let them send me to Siberia, I don't care !"

The women were screaming.   Drunken officials rushed into the cottage and separated father and son.   The father had an arm broken and the son's beard was torn out.   In the doorway a drunken girl was making violent love to an old besotted peasant.

"They are beasts !" said the young Tsar.

Another touch of his guide's hand and the young Tsar awoke in a new place.   It was the

14

office of the justice of the peace. A fat, bald-headed man, with a double chin and a chain round his neck, had just risen from his seat, and was reading the sentence in a loud voice, while a crowd of peasants stood behind the grating. There was a woman in rags in the crowd who did not rise. The guard gave her a push.

"Asleep! I tell you to stand up!" The woman rose.

"According to the decree of his Imperial Majesty——" the judge began reading the sentence. The case concerned that very woman. She had taken away half a bundle of oats as she was passing the thrashing-floor of a landowner. The justice of the peace sentenced her to two months imprisonment. The landowner whose oats had been stolen was among the audience. When the judge adjourned the court the landowner approached and shook hands, and the judge entered into conversation with him. The next case was about a stolen samovar. Then there was a trial about some timber which had been cut, to the detriment of the landowner. Some peasants were being tried for having assaulted the constable of the district.

When the young Tsar again lost consciousness, he awoke to find himself in the middle of a village, where he saw hungry, half-frozen children, and the wife of the man who had assaulted the constable broken down from overwork.

Then came a new scene.   In Siberia a tramp is being flogged with the lash, the direct result of an order issued by the Minister of Justice.   Again oblivion, and another scene.   The family of a Jewish watchmaker is evicted for being too poor. The children are crying, and the Jew, Isaaks, is greatly distressed.   At last they come to an arrangement, and he is allowed to stay on in the lodgings.

The chief of police takes a bribe : the governor of the province also secretly accepts a bribe.   Taxes are being collected.   In the village, while a cow is sold for payment, the police inspector is bribed by a factory owner, who thus escapes taxes altogether. And again a village court scene, and a sentence carried into execution—the lash !

"Ilia Vasilievich, could you not spare me that ?"

"No."

The peasant burst into tears.   "Well, of course Christ suffered, and He bids us suffer too."

Then other scenes.   The Stundists—a sect— being broken up and dispersed : the clergy refusing first to marry, then to bury a Protestant.   Orders given concerning the passage of the Imperial railway train : soldiers kept sitting in the mud—cold, hungry, and cursing. Decrees issued relating to the educational institutions of the Empress Mary Department. Corruption rampant in the foundling homes. An undeserved monument. Thieving among the clergy. The reinforcement of the political police. A woman being searched. A prison for convicts who are sentenced to be deported. A man being hanged for murdering a shop assistant.

Then the result of military discipline : soldiers wearing uniform and scoffing at it. A gipsy encampment. The son of a millionaire exempted from military duty, while the only support of a large family is forced to serve. The university : a teacher relieved of military service, while the most gifted musicians are compelled to perform it. Soldiers and their debauchery — and the spreading of disease.

Then a soldier who has made an attempt to desert : he is being tried. Another is on trial for striking an officer who has insulted his mother : he is put to death. Others, again, are tried for having refused to shoot. The runaway soldier sent to a disciplinary battalion and flogged to death. Another, who is guiltless, flogged, and his wounds sprinkled with salt till he dies. One of the superior officers stealing money belonging to the soldiers.   Nothing but drunkenness, debauchery, gambling, and arrogance on the part of the authorities.

What is the general condition of the people ? The children are half-starving and degenerate ; the houses are full of vermin ; an everlasting dull round of labour, of submission, and of sadness. On the other hand, ministers, governors of provinces—covetous, ambitious, full of vanity, and anxious to inspire fear.

" But where are men with human feelings ? "

" I will show you where they are."

Here is the cell of a woman in solitary confinement at Schlüsselburg. She is going mad. Here is another woman—a girl—indisposed, violated by soldiers. A man in exile, alone, embittered, half-dead. A prison for convicts condemned to hard labour, and women flogged. They are many.

Tens of thousands of the best people. Some shut up in prison, others ruined by false education, by the vain desire to bring them up as we wish. But not succeeding in this, whatever might have been is ruined as well, for it is made impossible. It is as if we were trying to make buckwheat out of corn sprouts by splitting the ears. One may spoil the corn, but one could never change it to buckwheat. Thus all the youth of the world, the entire younger generation, is being ruined.

But woe to those who destroy one of these little ones : woe to you if you destroy even one of them ! On your soul, however, are hosts of them, who have been ruined in your name, all of those over whom your power extends.

"But what can I do?" exclaimed the Tsar in despair. "I do not wish to torture, to flog, to corrupt, to kill any one ! I only want the welfare of all. Just as I yearn for happiness myself, so I want the world to be happy as well. Am I actually responsible for everything that is done in my name? What can I do? What am I to do to rid myself of such a responsibility? What can I do? I do not admit that the responsibility for all this is mine. If I felt myself responsible for one-hundredth part of it I would shoot myself on the spot. It would not be possible to live if that were true. But how can I put an end to all this evil? It is bound up with the very existence of the State. I am the head of the State ! What am I to do? Kill myself? Or abdicate? But that would mean renouncing my duty. O God, O God, help me ! " He burst into tears and awoke.

"How glad I am that it was only a dream," was his first thought.

But when he began to recollect what he had seen in his dream, and to compare it with actuality, he realized that the problem propounded to him in dream remained just as important and as insoluble now that he was awake. For the first time the young Tsar became aware of the heavy responsibility weighing on him, and was aghast. His thoughts no longer turned to the young queen and to the happiness he had anticipated for that evening, but became centred on the unanswerable question which hung over him : " What was to be done ? "

In a state of great agitation he arose and went into the next room. An old courtier, a co-worker and friend of his father's, was standing there in the middle of the room in conversation with the young Queen, who was on her way to join her husband. The young Tsar approached them, and addressing his conversation principally to the old courtier, told him what he had seen in his dream and what doubts the dream had left in his mind.

" That is a noble idea. It proves the rare nobility of your spirit," said the old man. " But forgive me for speaking frankly — you are too kind to be an emperor, and you exaggerate your responsibility. In the first place, the state of things is not as you imagine it to be. The people are not poor. They are well-to-do. Those who are poor are poor through their own fault. Only the guilty are punished, and if an unavoidable mistake does sometimes occur, it is like a thunderbolt—an accident, or the will of God. You have but one responsibility : to fulfil your task courageously and to retain the power that is given to you. You wish the best for your people and God sees that. As for the errors which you have committed unwittingly, you can pray for forgiveness, and God will guide you and pardon you. All the more because you have done nothing that demands forgiveness, and there never have been and never will be men possessed of such extraordinary qualities as you and your father. Therefore all we implore you to do is to live, and to reward our endless devotion and love with your favour, and every one, save scoundrels who deserve no happiness, will be happy."

"What do you think about that ?" the young Tsar asked his wife.

"I have a different opinion," said the clever young woman, who had been brought up in a free country. "I am glad you had that dream, and I agree with you that there are grave responsibilities resting upon you. I have often thought about it with great anxiety, and I think there is a simple means of casting off a part of the responsibility you are unable to bear, if not all of it. A large proportion of the power which is too heavy for you you should delegate to the people, to its representatives, reserving for yourself only the supreme control—that is, the general direction of the affairs of State."

The Queen had hardly ceased to expound her views, when the old courtier began eagerly to refute her arguments, and they started a polite but very heated discussion.

For a time the young Tsar followed their arguments, but presently he ceased to be aware of what they said, listening only to the voice of him who had been his guide in the dream, and who was now speaking audibly in his heart.

" You are not only the Tsar," said that voice, " but more. You are a human being, who only yesterday came into this world, and will perchance to-morrow depart out of it. Apart from your duties as a Tsar, of which that old man is now speaking, you have more immediate duties not by any means to be disregarded—human duties. Not the duties of a Tsar towards his subjects, which are only accidental, but an eternal duty, the duty of a man in his relation to God, the duty toward your own soul, which is to save it, and also, to serve God in establishing His kingdom on earth. You are not to be guided in your actions either by what has been or what will be, but only by what it is your own duty to do.

.   .   .   .   .   .

He opened his eyes—his wife was awakening him.   Which of the three courses the young Tsar chose will be told in fifty years.

THE END.